HANS, THE W
THE GOBBIN

A Play

by

ALAN CULLEN

SAMUEL FRENCH

LONDON

NEW YORK   TORONTO   SYDNEY   HOLLYWOOD

Please see page iv for further copyright information

HANS, THE WITCH AND THE GOBBIN

Produced at The Library Theatre, Manchester, on the 9th
December 1958, with the following cast of characters:

(in the order of their appearance)

GOB, a gobbin	*John Franklyn Robbins*
HANS, a student	*Stephen Macdonald*
ALICIA, a princess	*Patricia Regan*
CASTOR, a physician	*David Sumner*
SENNA, a physician	*Christopher Benjamin*
RUFUS, a king	*Bernard Kay*
SCRATCH, a secretary	*Michael Cox*
DAISY, a witch	*Cynthia Grenville*
MRS CRABTREE, a dowser	*Marah Stohl*
SYLVESTER, a swineherd	*David Mahlowe*
HANK, a pig	*Edwina Mitchell*
HUNK, another pig	*Brenda Elder*
QUEEN OF THE FOREST	*Cynthia Taylor*

Directed by DAVID SCASE
Décor by DAPHNE HART

SYNOPSIS OF SCENES

PROLOGUE
A Royal Park

ACT I
A room in the palace of King Rufus

ACT II
SCENE 1 The Forest
SCENE 2 Another part of the Forest
SCENE 3 The Queen of the Forest's Grotto

ACT III
SCENE 1 The Forest
SCENE 2 The Grotto
SCENE 3 The Forest

The time is after breakfast and before supper

PROLOGUE

SCENE—*A Royal Park.*

The scene is set down stage, in front of gauze tabs, with tree wings
R *and* L, *and a tree* LC.

When the CURTAIN *rises, the* GOBBIN *is practising a clog dance. He
wears a flat cap several sizes too small for his carroty-haired head, and
at the other end a pair of huge clogs. Between these extremities he is
something from another world, though quite what, it would be difficult to
determine. His clumsy dance is interrupted by the sound of whistling off* R.
THE GOBBIN *hastily and heavy-footedly conceals himself behind the
wing* L, *as the whistler approaches.* HANS *enters* R. *He is a young man
of pleasing appearance in a short, scholar's gown and carrying a small
pack over his shoulder. He crosses to* LC. *As he does so, a clock strikes and
he stops whistling.*

HANS. Ah, breakfast-time. (*He sits at the foot of the tree and takes
his frugal breakfast from his pack*) Let's see what we've got left.

(*The* GOBBIN, *unseen by* HANS, *emerges* L *and moves towards
Hans*)

Bread—cheese—and a bit of liver sausage.

(*The* GOBBIN *sneezes*)

(*Without looking up*) Bless you!

(*The* GOBBIN *hides behind the tree*)

A meal fit for a king, if the king is not too particular. And a royal
park to eat it in—provided the park-keeper doesn't see me.
What more could anyone want? (*He starts to eat*)

(*The* GOBBIN *emerges* R *of the tree, gliding heel-and-toe from behind
it, with a fatuous expression on his face.* HANS *looks at him in surprise.
The* GOBBIN *glides sideways to* C, *then goes into reverse and glides
back to Hans*)

GOBBIN. Hello.
HANS. Oh, hello.
GOBBIN (*dancing*) I bet you can't do this.
HANS. I'm sure I can't.
GOBBIN. Takes a lot of practice. Can you do *this?* (*He alters his
sideways shuffle to a more complex one*)
HANS. I don't think I would want to, thank you.
GOBBIN (*dancing*) I'm Gob.
HANS. *Are* you?

GOBBIN. Yes. I'm a Gobbin.

HANS. A—a Gobbin? Look, would you just keep still for a minute?

(*The* GOBBIN *stops dancing*)

You mean a goblin, surely?

GOBBIN. No, I mean a Gobbin. It's like a goblin, only bigger. And more gormless. (*He grins fatuously*) What's *your* name?

HANS. My name is Hans.

GOBBIN. I thought it would be.

HANS. Did you? Why?

GOBBIN. Oh, I don't know. I just thought. (*He moves behind the tree, peeps round the left side and grins*) Where are you going?

HANS. Nowhere in particular.

GOBBIN. I'm not, either.

HANS. I'm on holiday, as a matter of fact.

GOBBIN. Ooh, how luvly. Shall I tell you something?

HANS. What?

GOBBIN (*moving down* R *of the tree*) I like you. (*He shuffles right round in a circle and back*)

HANS. That's very nice of you.

GOBBIN. I bet you don't know why.

HANS. No, I don't.

GOBBIN. Because you've got some liver sausage.

HANS. Oh, would you like some?

GOBBIN (*quivering*) Yes, please.

HANS (*offering his packet of food*) Here you are, then—have that bit.

GOBBIN. That's the biggest.

HANS. Never mind—you have it.

GOBBIN (*leaning towards Hans*) Oh, I couldn't.

HANS. Go on, it's all right.

GOBBIN. Well, ask me again.

HANS. Please have this large piece of my sausage.

GOBBIN (*with alacrity*) Thanks. (*He jumps across to Hans, grabs the piece of sausage and swallows it almost in one movement*) Are you enjoying your holiday? (*He sits* R *of Hans*)

HANS. I am indeed. No more studies for a whole month. It's glorious.

GOBBIN. Studies? What's that?

HANS. Books. Learning things.

GOBBIN. You're not still at school at your age?

HANS. No, of course not.

GOBBIN. I thought!

HANS. I'm at the university. Medical student.

GOBBIN. Ee, aren't you clever? I'm a right Gobbin at anything like that. I can't even read, me.

HANS. Really?

GOBBIN. I can't write, neither.

HANS. They usually go together, I believe.

GOBBIN. Proper gobbin all right. (*He grins cheerfully*) I'll tell you what, though.

HANS. What?

GOBBIN. They don't diddle me so often.

HANS. I'm sure.

GOBBIN. I always get *my* ha'penny back on the bottle.

HANS (*laughing*) That doesn't surprise me. By the way, what are you doing here?

GOBBIN (*dropping his head between his knees; coyly*) Shan't tell you.

HANS. Why not? I told you about myself.

GOBBIN (*looking up*) I don't like. (*He drops his head*)

HANS. All right, I'm not all that curious.

GOBBIN (*sitting bolt upright*) Give me a bit of your cheese and I'll tell you.

HANS. There. (*He hands a piece of cheese to the Gobbin*)

(*The* GOBBIN *bolts the cheese, takes another piece and grins*)

Not doing so badly for a Gobbin, are you?

GOBBIN. Oh, go on. You make me feel proper awful.

HANS. You still haven't told me what you're doing here.

GOBBIN (*bashfully*) I was waiting for you.

HANS. For me? But I don't understand. How did you know I was coming?

GOBBIN (*airily*) Oh, there's ways and means. I'm your fettler.

HANS. My what?

GOBBIN. Your fettler. I have to fettle things for you, like.

HANS. I *think* I understand. But why?

GOBBIN. Because you gave me some of your liver sausage.

HANS. What if I hadn't given you any?

GOBBIN (*leaning back*) Oh, I should have turned awkward. I can be proper conny-west when I like, you know. There's all sorts I could have done, like—er—nails in your shoes, grit in your eye, soap on your stairs—oh, there's all sorts. And you'd never have known it was me.

HANS. I see.

GOBBIN (*pointing at Hans*) I'm going to make you famous.

HANS. Oh. You won't find that very easy. To be famous you have to have something special about you, and I haven't. I'm very ordinary, I'm afraid.

(*The* GOBBIN *helps himself to another piece of cheese*)

GOBBIN. You won't be when I've finished with you. You're a bit of a day-dreamer on the quiet, aren't you?

HANS. Yes, a bit. I think everybody is.

GOBBIN. Go on, you know you are. You weren't half romancing to yourself coming down the lane just now.

HANS. How do you know that?

GOBBIN (*nudging Hans*) I know. Maidens in distress and all sorts, eh?

HANS. Perhaps I was. There's no harm in that, is there?

GOBBIN (*rising*) I'll show you one if you like.

HANS. What, a maiden in distress? (*He rises*)

GOBBIN (*rising*) 'M. A princess, too. Look, I'll show you. (*He moves down* R) Turn away and shut your eyes.

(HANS *faces front and closes his eyes*)

(*He faces front*) Are they shut?

HANS. Yes.

GOBBIN (*turning to Hans*) They're not.

HANS. Yes, they are.

GOBBIN. Don't open them till I tell you. (*He faces front, points over his right shoulder with his left hand, points over his left shoulder with his right hand and recites*)

"Gobbin this road,
Gobbin that road,
Gobbin, gobbin, gobbin."

(*He spits over his crossed wrists for good measure and turns to Hans*) You can look now.

(HANS *opens his eyes, turns and faces up* C. *A spot comes up behind the gauze, revealing* PRINCESS ALICIA *lying motionless on her couch and looking very beautiful*)

HANS. Is—is that the princess?

GOBBIN. Yes. She's proper poorly.

HANS. How beautiful she is; so delicate—as white and delicate as a snowflake. What is her name?

GOBBIN. Alicia.

HANS. Alicia . . .

GOBBIN. The King wanted her christened Sar' Alice but the Queen didn't think that was posh enough, so they called her Alicia, instead.

HANS. But why do they leave her like that? Why don't they do something about finding a cure?

GOBBIN. Oh, they have done. But nobody knows what's the matter with her. Except me. I'm only a gobbin, but I know.

HANS. Then why don't you go and tell them?

GOBBIN (*crossing to* L *of Hans*) Sh! You'll wake her up. (*He turns Hans to face front*) Turn round again.

HANS (*turning to face up* C) Oh, not yet. Keep her there a little longer.

GOBBIN (*turning Hans to face front*) Turn round, I said.

(HANS *turns reluctantly and shuts his eyes*)

Eyes shut?

HANS. Yes.

GOBBIN (*repeating his spell*)
          "Gobbin this road,
          Gobbin that road,
          Gobbin, gobbin, gobbin."

(*The spot fades and the* PRINCESS *disappears*)

You can look now. (*He moves* L)

HANS (*picking up his pack and following the Gobbin*) Gob, you must take me to her. At once.

GOBBIN (*crossing to* R) Hey, hold on. You're not a proper doctor yet, you know.

(HANS *follows the Gobbin to* R)

How do you know you can make her better?

HANS. I can try. It's terrible to see her like that.

GOBBIN. You know what the King will do to you if you fail, don't you? (*He draws his finger across his throat*)

HANS. I don't care. I've got to try.

GOBBIN. All right. Come here and I'll tell you what's the matter with her. (*He whispers in Hans's ear*) It's right.

HANS. So that's why they can't find a cure.

GOBBIN. Do you still want to go to her?

HANS. More than ever.

GOBBIN. Right. Shut your eyes again and you'll be there in two ticks.

(*The lights dim quickly to* BLACK-OUT)

Tick, tick.

HANS *and the* GOBBIN *exit* R, *the tree is struck, the gauze* TABS *open, and the lights go up on the next scene.*

ACT I

SCENE—*A room in the palace of King Rufus.*
The room, pre-set behind the gauze TABS *of the Prologue, has a low rostrum up* C *backed by tall french windows. Below the rostrum is a tree cut-cloth, the sides of which are concealed in this Act by wings flanking the rostrum. The upstage folds of the wings are french windows and the downstage folds are arches. Behind the cut-cloth there is a pair of gauze* TABS. *Down stage there are wings* R *and* L. *On the rostrum is a couch with the head up stage. A small stool is* L *of the couch.*

When the gauze TABS *open, the* PRINCESS ALICIA *is reclining listlessly on the couch.* CASTOR *is standing* R *of the couch.* SENNA *is seated on the stool* L *of the couch. Both are sounding the Princess.*

SENNA (*rising*) I still maintain, Castor, that the Princess's condition is one of psycho-physical lassitude, occasioned by the over-agenization of the starchy content of her diet. (*He turns the couch on its castors so that the head is* R) In other words, it's the bread we get these days.

CASTOR. Rubbish! The trouble with you, Senna, is that you read too many books. Purges and plasters, my boy, purges and plasters—(*he returns the couch to its original position*) they cure anything.

SENNA (*turning the couch with the head* R) Well, they haven't been very successful with the Princess so far.

CASTOR (*returning the couch to its original position*) Neither has your psycho-physical patent diet, Senna. In fact, Her Highness gets worse instead of better. Anyhow, we shall never agree. (*He moves below the couch and sits on the downstage end*)

(SENNA *moves below the couch and sits* L *of Castor on the downstage end*)

The point is what are we to tell the King this morning?

SENNA. True. However much we differ in private, we must present a united front in public, if either of us is to continue in office. What do you suggest should be the general lines of our report for today?

CASTOR. Play safe, Senna. From the sound of his voice this morning, even at a distance, the King needs handling with tact. (*He rises and stands* R *of the couch*)

(SENNA *rises and stands* L *of the couch*)

The non-committal line, I think, with a touch of confident optimism. Hm?

(SENNA *and* CASTOR *tuck the Princess in, turn the couch with its head to* R *and pat the Princess's cheeks*)

SENNA. Right, Castor. Comfortable night?
CASTOR (*bowing*) *Fairly* comfortable.
SENNA. Temperature about normal?
CASTOR (*bowing*) *About* normal.
SENNA. Slight improvement, perhaps?
CASTOR (*bowing*) *Very* slight improvement.
SENNA. No cause for anxiety?
CASTOR (*bowing*) No *immediate* cause for anxiety.
SENNA. Good. If he makes anything out of that, he's a better man than I am.
KING (*off*) Keep close behind me, Scratch. Left, right—left, right.

(CASTOR *and* SENNA, *side by side, circle down* RC, *up* LC *and turn.*
    The KING *marches on* R. *He is in none too good a temper.* CASTOR *and* SENNA *bow.*
    SCRATCH *marches in close behind the King*)

(*He marches to* C) Left, right. Keep your head up. (*He halts abruptly*)

(SCRATCH *crashes into the King*)

Sorry. (*He turns to the Princess*)

(SCRATCH *continues and marches off* R)

(*He stares hard at the Princess for a moment, then turns to Castor and Senna*) Well?

(CASTOR *and* SENNA *bow profoundly*)

CASTOR (*crossing down* R) Good morning, Your Majesty. (*He bows*)
SENNA (*crossing to* R *of the King*) Nice day, Your Majesty. (*He bows*)
KING. Never mind that. How is the Princess?
CASTOR. Well, she has passed a fairly comfortable night, Your Majesty.
SENNA. She has practically no temperature this morning, Your Majesty.
CASTOR. In fact, we can report a slight improvement in her general condition.
SENNA. *Only very* slight, of course. And there is no cause for anxiety. (*He bows and remains down*)
CASTOR. No immediate cause, that is. (*He bows and remains down*)
KING. In fact, she's no better, and I never expected she would be as long as you are my court physicians.

(CASTOR *and* SENNA *straighten up and look at each other*)
For a whole year now she has lain on that couch and has neither spoken a word nor taken the least interest in anything that goes on about her. And you don't even know what's the matter with her. Well, I know what's wrong with her.

(CASTOR *and* SENNA *look at the* King)

She's bored, that's all. Bored. And who wouldn't be, with a pair of fatuous incompetents like you two fussing about.
CASTOR (*bowing*) We can only do our best, Your Majesty.
SENNA. All that could be done has been done, Your Majesty.
KING. Very well, from now on I handle her case myself. You are discharged.
CASTOR⎱
SENNA ⎰(*together; bowing*) Thank you, Your Majesty.
KING (*with a step towards them*) Don't be impertinent.

(CASTOR *and* SENNA *spin away up* R)

And stop bobbing up and down. You'll make me dizzy, and I'll wager you couldn't even cure that. (*He calls*) Scratch.

(SCRATCH *enters* R. *He carries a notebook and pencil*)

SCRATCH. Yes, Your Majesty?
KING. Take a proclamation.
SCRATCH. Yes, Your Majesty.

(*The* KING *circles down* C *and up* R *to Castor and Senna.* SCRATCH *follows him, busily writing*)

KING (*to Castor and Senna*) I told you all along the Princess was only bored.

(CASTOR *and* SENNA *back up* L)

(*He crosses to* C) Well, now I'll prove it. All she wants is something to titillate her fancy.
SCRATCH (R *of the* King) I can't spell "titillate".
KING. T, I, T, I double L . . . What are you talking about? (*He smacks Scratch's book to the floor*) I didn't tell you to take that down.
SCRATCH (*picking up his book*) I beg your pardon, Your Majesty. I waste so much paper that way. I do wish you'd say "right" or something, then I'd know when to begin.
KING. Right.
SCRATCH. Now?
KING. Yes, now.
SCRATCH. Right.
KING (*moving down* C) Give me patience! "To all my loyal subjects, greeting. Be it known herewith that whosoever shall

effect a cure for the Princess's melancholy condition . . ." Er—
let me see, how far have I got?

(CASTOR *picks up the stool and sets it down* C)

SCRATCH (*busily writing*) If you don't mind, sir—not quite so
fast.
KING. Eh? Oh, all right. (*He sits on the stool*) Where was I up
to? Read it all back to me.
SCRATCH (*reading*) "Give me patience to all my loyal subjects
greetings. Be it known herewith that whosoever shall effect a
cure for the Princess's melancholy condition—er—let me see, how
far have I got?"
KING. Oh, you stupid scribe. (*He rises*) Give me that. (*He
snatches the book and pencil from Scratch and strikes out some of the
writing*) There. (*He returns the book and pencil to Scratch and puts a
foot up on the stool*) Now write.
SCRATCH. Right.
KING. ". . . shall be granted . . ." Shall be granted—ah, now,
there's a point. What shall we offer as a reward?
SCRATCH. Half the kingdom?
KING. She's not *that* ill.
SCRATCH. I was only trying to help. Besides, it's the usual
thing.
CASTOR (*moving to* R *of the King*) The office of Lord High
Constable? It's vacant at the moment.
KING. Rubbish! That means an income as well, and I can't
afford it. That's why it's vacant.
SENNA (*moving to* L *of the King*) Whatever they ask?
KING. That's the most stupid suggestion of the lot.
SENNA. Not really, Your Majesty. Nobody would dare to ask
for what they really wanted. They would simply leave it to you,
and you could just give them any little thing you fancy—a medal
or something.
KING. H'm. Anything my Majesty fancies. You may be right.
In fact, I'm sure you're right. Senna, you are re-employed. (*He
sits on the stool*)

(SENNA *and* CASTOR *stand behind the King*)

SENNA. Thank you, Your Majesty. It was nothing, really.
KING. Write, Scratch. ". . . shall be granted whatever they
ask. Signed, Rufus Rex." (*He rises*) Have that promulgated
immediately.

(SCRATCH *picks up the stool and puts it up* C. CASTOR *and* SENNA
move up RC)

SCRATCH. Yes, Your Majesty.

(HANS *enters up* L.

SCRATCH *exits hurriedly up* L, *colliding with* HANS *who stands waiting to be noticed*)

KING (*to Senna and Castor*) But mind you, your appointments are continued only under sufferance. Unless there is a marked improvement in the standard of your ministrations, out you both go. (*He turns, sees Hans and moves up* C) Who are you?

HANS. My name is Hans, Your Majesty. I am a poor student of the University of Wurstberg. I am here in response to your proclamation.

KING (*moving to* R *of Hans*) Do you mean the proclamation I just issued?

HANS. Yes, Your Majesty.

KING. You've been remarkably quick about it. It isn't even promulgated yet.

HANS. I happened to be passing the window as Your Majesty was dictating it. I came straight in. I don't know if you are aware of it, but Your Majesty has a remarkably penetrating voice.

KING (*turning to Castor and Senna*) Castor, why have you never told me I shout?

CASTOR. I wouldn't call it shouting, Your Majesty—just the voice of authority.

KING. Rubbish! He's quite right. I do shout. He's the first man I've met with the courage to tell me so to my face. (*He turns to Hans*) Young man, I like you.

HANS (*bowing*) I am honoured, Your Majesty.

KING. As long as you go on telling me the truth to my face, I shall continue to like you. Remember it.

HANS. I will, sir.

KING. Now then, about the Princess. What makes you think you can cure her illness? Are you a doctor?

HANS. Not yet, Your Majesty. But I rather think I have diagnosed the Princess's condition from her symptoms.

(CASTOR *and* SENNA *look at each other*)

KING. But you haven't examined her even. How do you know what her symptoms are?

HANS. They are common knowledge, Your Majesty. Things like that cannot be kept secret for very long.

KING (*looking at Castor and Senna*) They could be if certain people kept their mouths shut a bit more than they do.

SENNA. Your Majesty surely doesn't think that Castor and I . . . ?

KING. I don't think, I know. (*He turns to Hans*) Well, young man, what is the matter with her?

HANS. May I look at her Highness?

KING (*moving to* R *of the couch*) You have our permission.

(HANS *moves above the couch*)

HANS (*gazing at the Princess*) She is even more beautiful than people say.

KING. That is neither here nor there. How much longer are you going to stand and make sheep's eyes at her?

HANS. I'm sorry. (*He passes his hand in front of the Princess's eyes*)

(*The* PRINCESS *does not blink*)

H'm. (*He lifts her hand and lets it fall slowly back into place*) What is your name?

PRINCESS (*slowly*) I—I don't know.

HANS. How old are you?

CASTOR (*scandalized*) What a thoroughly unprofessional question.

(CASTOR *and* SENNA *pace down* R)

SENNA. Hopeless bedside manner.

KING. Oh, be quiet. (*To Hans*) She's nineteen and a half.

(CASTOR *and* SENNA *pace up* R)

HANS (*rapt*) Nineteen—and a half . . . (*He moves* L)

KING (*coughing significantly*) Hrrrm!

(HANS *pulls himself together and turns thoughtfully to the King*)

Well? What do you think?

HANS (*moving down* L) That she is suffering from a complete loss of memory, as I thought at first, is quite clear, but there is something else—something I'm not quite sure about. (*He moves to* L *of the couch*) Yes, Your Majesty, I am almost certain that the Princess has been bewitched.

KING. Bewitched? Who by?

CASTOR. "By whom?"

KING (*turning to Castor*) You . . . !

HANS. That I cannot say. But there is a distinct aura of magic suspended in the air about her.

KING. Are you sure it isn't camphorated oil?

HANS. I said "aura", not "odour".

KING. Oh. And you think this bewitching has made her lose her memory? (*He sits on the end of the couch*)

HANS. I rather fancy her memory is not so much lost as stolen.

KING. Stolen? This is all most alarming. Do you mean to tell me that even our memories are not safe inside our heads these days? I never heard of such a thing. (*To Castor and Senna*) Have you ever heard of such a thing? I've never heard of such a thing.

HANS. It is my considered opinion, Your Majesty. The problem now is to discover who has it.

SENNA (*moving to* R *of the King*) It might help if we were to ask her when she saw it last.

KING (*rising*) Don't be a fool, Senna. It isn't the sort of thing anyone would just leave around.

CASTOR (*moving to* R *of Senna*) But who would want someone else's memory? It doesn't make sense.

HANS (*moving* LC) Spells very often don't. Sometimes they're just done for spite. Can you think of anyone who had a grudge against the Princess, Your Majesty?

KING (*moving up* R *of the couch*) Grudge against her? Certainly not. She is held in the greatest esteem by the entire nation—or I know the reason why. She is universally loved—by royal decree.

HANS. That makes our task a little more difficult.

SENNA (*crossing to* L *of the King*) If it's a question of Lost and Found, isn't it a matter for the Chief of Police?

KING. I sacked him two days ago. The last time the crown jewels were stolen he started by taking *my* fingerprints.

HANS (*moving down* LC) I'm afraid ordinary methods will be of little use in a case like this. We are dealing with witchcraft, and we must employ witchcraft ourselves in order to fight against it.

(CASTOR *and* SENNA *move up* R)

KING (*moving to* R *of Hans*) That makes sense, at any rate. Set a witch to catch a witch, is that it?

HANS. Exactly. All Your Majesty has to do now is to find a co-operative witch who will undertake the task.

KING. That, I'm afraid, will not be easy.

HANS. But surely there must be plenty of witches among Your Majesty's subjects only too anxious to put "By Royal Appointment" over the doors of their hovels?

(SCRATCH *enters* L *and creeps across to Senna and Castor*)

KING. No. You see, I had a kind of purge a few years ago. They were becoming something of a nuisance, what with whizzing about all night on broomsticks and keeping everyone awake—and then there was the smell, you know.

HANS. The smell?

KING. Yes. Sulphur and brimstone. The city was full of it. I had to do something, so I withdrew their licences. Put them out of business.

HANS. What did they do, then?

KING. Oh, various things. Opened teashops, most of them. One or two became landladies, if I remember rightly. Anyhow, they all went, and now I wouldn't know where to turn to find a witch, I really wouldn't.

SCRATCH. May I make a suggestion, Your Majesty?

(CASTOR *and* SENNA *attempt to stop Scratch*)

KING. I don't see why not. But if it makes sense I shall be very much surprised.

SCRATCH. My auntie.

KING. What about your auntie?

SCRATCH. My aunt Mrs Crabtree. She might be able to help.

KING. Are you trying to tell me that you have an aunt by the name of Mrs Crabtree who is a witch? Because if so, she must be practising without a licence, and she'll find herself in jail if she isn't careful.

SCRATCH (*moving to* R *of the King*) Oh, no. Not a witch. She's a dowser.

KING. A what?

SCRATCH. A dowser. She dowses.

KING. I dare say. If she's a relation of yours, she's capable of anything.

HANS. I think your secretary means that his aunt is a water-diviner, Your Majesty.

KING. Water-diviner? What in the world has that got to do with it? Unless you're suggesting the Princess has water on the brain.

SCRATCH. I said it was only a suggestion. There's no need to be sarcastic about it.

HANS. It might be worth a trial, Your Majesty. Dowsers have been known to find all sorts of things. Some of them have very extraordinary powers.

KING. Some people seem to have very extraordinary aunts. Whoever would have thought, to look at Scratch, that he had an aunt who dowsed?

SCRATCH. Your Majesty embarrasses me.

KING. Well, I suppose it will do no harm to send for this Mrs Crabtree. (*He moves down* R) Have her brought here at once.

SCRATCH. You underestimate her, sire. Nobody sends for my aunt. She might condescend to come if she were approached in the right manner, but any attempts at coercion would be futile.

KING (*turning sharply to Scratch*) Scratch!

SCRATCH. Yes, Your Majesty?

KING. Get that woman here in five minutes, or you'll find you've been underestimating *me*. Condescend indeed!

SCRATCH. I'll do my best, but I can't promise anything.

KING. Oh, yes, you can.

(SCRATCH *runs off* L)

(*He moves to Hans*) One of these days, that secretary will find himself pinned neatly to one of his documents and marked "For immediate despatch". "Nobody sends for *my* aunt!" Who does this uncoercible Mrs Dowsing Crabtree think she is? Hrrrmph! (*He moves to Castor and Senna*) Let me know when she arrives.

CASTOR }
SENNA } *together; bowing* {   Yes, Your Majesty. (*They remain
                                  bowed*)
KING. Hans, you will come with me. I want to talk to you.
HANS. Yes, Your Majesty.

(*The* KING *exits* L.
  HANS *follows him off*)

CASTOR (*slowly straightening up*) That was a near thing, Senna.
SENNA (*slowly straightening up*) *Too* near. You almost had us
sacked for good.
CASTOR. *I* did? Now, wait a minute, it was your fault.
SENNA. Well, I like that. (*He brings the stool down* C) Who was
it got us unsacked again, I'd like to know?

(*They both sit on the stool*)

CASTOR. Never mind that now. Senna, we're in trouble.
SENNA. What do you mean?
CASTOR. I mean if this Mrs Crabtree is a success, who's going
to get the credit for it?
SENNA. Scratch, I suppose.
CASTOR. Rubbish! This man Hans is. It was he who started it
all.
SENNA. Well?
CASTOR. Well, don't you see what a precarious position we're
in? If he succeeds in curing the Princess, the King will make
him Court Physician, and we shall be out on our respective ears.
SENNA. After all our years of faithful service—(*he gestures and
knocks Castor off the stool*) thrown aside like a worn-out stethoscope.
They can't do this to us, Castor. (*He rises and helps Castor to rise*)
CASTOR. What are you talking about? They haven't done it
yet.
SENNA. Oh. Then what's all the fuss about?
CASTOR. It's only that we must keep our wits about us. We
may get a chance of being there first, and if we do, we must jump
at it.
SENNA. Jump at it. Yes, that's what we must do.
CASTOR. Have you any idea what I'm talking about?
SENNA. None whatever.
CASTOR. What I mean is we must . . .

(*The* PRINCESS *sighs and sits up*)

SENNA. Sh!
CASTOR. What's the matter?
SENNA (*moving to* R *of the couch*) The Princess——

(CASTOR *moves to* L *of the couch*)

—look, she's sitting up and taking notice.

CASTOR. She's sitting up, certainly, but she doesn't seem to notice much.

SENNA. She looks as though she's listening for something.

CASTOR. I think there's someone coming. Quick, hide.

(SENNA *hides behind the french window up* R. CASTOR *hides behind the french window up* L.

DAISY CROWFOOT *appears outside the window up* C, *opens it and enters. She is a fantastic figure, a witch unmistakably. She is a crazily restless creature, whose every movement expresses utter eccentricity, as do the tones of her voice and her cracked, irregular speech. She cannot be too odd. She is singing a crazy jingle*)

DAISY (*as she enters*) "Here I come
       Heel and toe;
       There I go;
       In and out
       And roundabout
(*She moves down* C)
       Hither and yon
       Off and on—
       Before you know it
       I've been and gone."

Aha! All alone, I see. That's the way. (*She looks off* R *and* L) Daisy doesn't like being interrupted. (*She swoops across the room and perches herself on the couch by the side of the Princess*) Good morning, dearie. Dearie, dearie me, whoops and fiddle-faddle, but you are looking seedy this a.m.; a.m.—ante-meridiem—she was my maternal auntie, you know, and what a character. Whoops and tiddy-fol-fol. How do you feel?

PRINCESS. I—I don't feel anything at all.

DAISY. That's the way, alackaday. Everything going according to plan; plan, plan, plan, rataplan, Daisy Crowfoot's lovely plan, but you know our Daisy, don't you, dearie?

PRINCESS. Yes, I know you. You have something that belongs to me. Something important. When are you going to give it back to me?

DAISY (*rocking herself*) Aha! When? "When, oh, when?" said the little red hen, and nobody knew the answer.

PRINCESS. I don't know what it is you have taken from me—I can't remember—I can't remember anything—but I must have it back. I must. Don't you understand?

DAISY (*rising*) "Must", she said, "Must". "Little man, little man, must is not a word to be used before quinces," she said. (*She moves down* C)

(CASTOR *and* SENNA *reappear*)

Hey nonny no *indeed!* But I digress, as the man said when he walked over the edge of the cliff. (*She crosses to* L) "Let us, my dear, discuss this thing on a business footing, 'footing it featly', as the poet says . . ."

PRINCESS. Oh, please talk sensibly for a moment, *please.*

(DAISY *paces up* C. CASTOR *and* SENNA *freeze*)

DAISY. "Sense", she says. (*She turns to the audience*) Why talk sense when nonsense is nicer?

PRINCESS. I don't know what is the matter with me, but I only know I shall not be well again until you give me back what you have taken from me.

DAISY. Now we are getting down to it. Down a down and a derry derry down. (*She moves up* R) Daisy is not a thief, you know. Oh, dear, no. She pays. Daisy pays. I'm offering you the best price on the market for your memory. (*She sits on the stool*)

PRINCESS. My memory?

DAISY. That's it. Daisy has a conscience. Heigh-ho! (*She rises*)

(CASTOR *and* SENNA *disappear behind the doors*)

Daisy offers you the full value and a little bit more. Here it is —as full of magic as a pie is full of meat. (*She produces a snuff-box from her pocket*) Shall I tell you what it does? Oh, it's scrumptious, scrumptious magic. I'll show you. You open the box, take a sniff of punch, a snuff of pinch, a pinch of snuff and say the magic words. (*She suits the action to the words, takes a pinch of snuff, sneezes, and says the magic words*)

(CASTOR's *and* SENNA's *heads appear round the doors*)

> "Yesterday's is what it was
> Tomorrow's is what it will be
> Today's is what it is
> What is it?"

Now, we shall have all the news, you'll see. (*She sits on the stool*)

(*A breathless, gossipy voice appears to issue from the box*)

VOICE (*off*) Here is the news, and you'll never guess what.

(CASTOR's *and* SENNA's *heads disappear*)

His Majesty the King is reported from an authoritative source to be seeking the advice and assistance of——

(CASTOR's *and* SENNA's *heads slowly reappear*)

—who do you think—Mrs Crabtree, the well-known water-diviner, in an attempt to trace the cause of the Princess's mysterious malady. From what I can gather . . .

(DAISY *snaps the box shut in alarm and puts it on the floor.* CASTOR's *and* SENNA's *heads disappear*)

DAISY (*rising*) Oh, mischief, thou art afoot. (*She paces around the stool*) Oh, the deceitfulness of some people. Crabtree, eh? So that's the way it goes. Goose pimples all over! Oh, my disgracious me! Quills on the porpentine, as the poet says. (*She sings*)

> "Heel and toe,
> Here I go;
> Hither and yon,
> And off and on,
> Before you know it,
> I've been and gone!"

Whoops, Liza.

(Daisy, *her agitation increasing, exits* L, *leaving the snuff-box on the floor. The* Princess *relapses into her somnambulist state and lies back on the couch.* Castor *and* Senna *emerge from their hiding-places and move* C)

Castor. Well, what do you make of that?

Senna. Certifiable, definitely certifiable.

Castor. Certifiable nothing. She knows what she's doing. *She's* the one who has stolen the Princess's memory.

Senna. But, of course. I gathered that much. But she's stark, raving mad, all the same.

Castor. Who cares? The point is, we now know who it is, and the others don't.

(*They move down* C)

If we play our cards properly, we can get the reward and set ourselves up for life.

Senna. But what about Crabtree? Daisy is obviously afraid of her.

Castor. We must put her off the trail. Confuse the issue.

Senna. How are we going to do that?

(Castor *moves* LC. Senna *moves* RC)

Castor. I don't know yet. (*He looks towards the Princess*) We must wait and see. (*He sees the snuff-box*) Ah!

Senna. Look! She's left something behind. (*He picks up the snuff-box and hands it to Castor*)

Castor. It's the magic snuff-box. I'll keep it. It might come in useful.

King (*off* L) And there, my dear Hans, you have the entire case-history.

Senna. Careful. They're coming back. Hide it.

(Castor *pockets the snuff-box. He and* Senna *move down* R *and confer*)

King (*off*) And I think you will agree it is a most unusual and baffling case.

(*The* King *and* Hans *enter* L. Castor *and* Senna *pretend to be continuing a learned conversation*)

CASTOR. But I think you will agree with me, my dear Senna, that there is an undeniable affinity between the Princess's and the famous case of Arabella Slipstitch, quoted in full by Professor Mortadella of the University of Split—or was it Splot?

SENNA. Slosh, I think.

CASTOR. You are right; Splow, it was . . .

KING (crossing to Castor and Senna) Well? Any developments?

SENNA (bowing) None to speak of, Your Majesty. There is no cause for anxiety.

CASTOR (bowing) No *immediate* cause, that is . . .

KING. Now, don't start that all over again.

(SCRATCH enters L).

I'm in a sacking mood today, and don't you forget it.

CASTOR (bowing) No, Your Majesty.

SENNA (bowing) Thank you, Your Majesty.

SCRATCH. Your Majesty, allow me to introduce my aunt, Mrs Crabtree.

(MRS CRABTREE *sweeps in* L *and stops for a moment. Intense is perhaps the adjective which best describes her. Her dress and cape are made of thick tweed which she has spun and woven herself, and she has on a quantity of lumpy, hand-made jewellery, mostly in pewter. She carries a forked hazel stick*)

KING. Ah, Mrs Crabtree. This is indeed a pleasure. (*He holds out his hand and crosses towards Mrs Crabtree*)

(MRS CRABTREE *holds out her hand, crosses towards the King, misses his hand, marches straight on and shakes hands with Castor. The* KING *goes straight ahead and shakes hands with Scratch.* MRS CRABTREE *and the* KING *stop, look round, turn and move* C)

MRS CRABTREE (*facing front*) Don't speak to me. I must imbibe the radiations whilst they are still fresh. (*She stands, head up, nostrils wide, eyes bulging, and visibly concentrating*) The radiations are like a rich odour, strongest at first perception, then weakening gradually as one's senses grow accustomed to them.

SCRATCH (*moving to* L *of the King*) Isn't she terrific?

MRS CRABTREE. Silence, Euripides.

KING. Euripides? Scratch, don't tell me your name has been Euripides all these years, and I never knew.

(*All except* SCRATCH *laugh*)

SCRATCH (*moving* L) I . . . Auntie . . .

MRS CRABTREE. Silence! I can feel it growing upon me. It's here in this room—(*she becomes agitated*) magic, unmistakable magic.

(CASTOR *and* SENNA *cringe*)

Seek it, find it, search it out. (*The hazel twig begins to twitch and jerk in her hands*) Oh! Oh! This is exceptional. Such positive results in so short a time. (*She circles* R) What an article I shall write for *The Witch Finders' Bulletin*. (*She is wrestling for dear life with the hazel twig, which is pulling her round*) We're away! Oh, splendid manifestation! The hunt! The hunt is up! Seek it, find it, search it out! Oh, rapturous fulfilment.

(*The twig pulls her in the direction of Castor and Senna*)

CASTOR. Oh, crikey! (*In a loud whisper*) Senna, it's the box. She's on to the box. What shall I do?

(CASTOR *and* SENNA *dodge up* C)

SENNA. Get rid of it, quickly!

(CASTOR *takes the snuff-box from his pocket and transfers it to* SENNA, *who holds it like a hot potato*)

Not me, you fool. Oh!

(*The twig is approaching Senna now, with* MRS CRABTREE *in full cry.* SENNA *hastily dodges behind Hans and contrives to slip the snuff-box into Hans' pocket as he goes by*)

MRS CRABTREE. Success!

(*The twig, with* MRS CRABTREE *on the end of it, finishes up jabbed against Hans' stomach.* CASTOR *and* SENNA *cross and stand down* R)

Success, Your Majesty! (*She lowers the twig and points like an avenging Justice at Hans*) There is your man. I accuse him in the name of the League of Vigilance Against Witchcraft and Necromantic Practices. Let justice be done. (*Exhausted with her efforts, she sways and sags at the knees. Weakly*) Euripides, my smelling salts, quickly.

(SCRATCH *goes to* MRS CRABTREE, *helps her to the stool, seats her and fans her*)

SCRATCH. Magnificent, Auntie. You showed 'em. You've never done better.

HANS. Your Majesty, I protest. This is utter injustice. I have absolutely nothing to do with the Princess's illness. She's mistaken.

KING. Silence! I—I don't know what to think, I really don't. (*He moves to Mrs Crabtree*) Madam, I feel I cannot accept the results of this remarkable performance of yours without a little more thought. It—it was all so sudden.

MRS CRABTREE (*rallying*) Thought! What has thought to do with it? (*She rises and moves down* C) We are dealing here with something beyond thought, beyond the rational. We must believe in it without understanding it. We must have faith.

(SCRATCH *moves the stool up* R)

KING. Yes, yes, that's all very well, but . . .

MRS CRABTREE. Just a moment. Please allow me to finish. I never fail. Kindly take a look at that. (*She shows the King a badge in her lapel*) You see what it says? "League of Vigilance. Witchfinder First Class and Dowser Extraordinary. Ten years' loyal service." And on the back—"Awarded to Hypatia Crabtree for outstanding zeal in the pursuit of witches. She always gets her witch." There! Those are my credentials, King Rufus, and I say again—that is your man.

HANS (*moving to* L *of Mrs Crabtree*) Now, look here, Mrs Dowser . . .

MRS CRABTREE. "Crabtree", if you don't mind.

HANS. Mrs Crabtree, then. Whatever your talents may be as a water-diviner, as a finder of witches they are grossly overrated. I am neither witch nor warlock nor magician nor necromancer nor anything else. I am a simple medical student on vacation from the University of Wurstberg doing the best I can to assist the Princess towards a cure. Do I *look* like a male witch?

MRS CRABTREE (*advancing on Hans*) As to that——

(HANS *retreats*)

—I can assure you that appearances can be very deceptive— (*she moves towards Scratch*) as Euripides can bear me out.

(CASTOR *and* SENNA *begin to creep out* R)

(*To Scratch*) You remember Mother Mintdrop, I expect?

SCRATCH. Oh, yes, Auntie, I remember her.

(MRS CRABTREE *moves towards* CASTOR *and* SENNA *who creep back to their places*)

Harmless as a fly, she seemed, until you got on to her. She used to give all us children mint-balls to suck.

MRS CRABTREE. She finished up in the ducking-stool for all that. Hypatia Crabtree always gets her witch. (*She turns to the King and advances on him*) It was proved beyond doubt——

(*The* KING *retreats up* L)

—that she turned herself into a bluebottle regularly every Tuesday, and Thursdays as well in Lent. But she paid the price when I got after her with my little hazel wand. (*She moves* C)

KING (*moving to* L *of Mrs Crabtree*) This is getting us nowhere, Mrs C. The case of Mother Coughdrop . . .

MRS CRABTREE. "Mintdrop."

KING. Coughdrop or Gumdrop, what's the difference? It has nothing to do with the case in point. Unless I have positive proof of Hans dealing in witchcraft, I refuse to take any action against him.

HANS. Thank you, Your Majesty.

CASTOR (*crossing above the King to* L *of him*) May I say a word, sire?

(SENNA *moves to* R *of Mrs Crabtree.* HANS *moves down* LC)

KING. If you must.

CASTOR. Perhaps Mrs Crabtree is not so far wrong after all. If we can induce Master Hans to perform a piece of magic for us, will you believe her, then?

KING. I suppose so—yes. What are you getting at, Castor?

CASTOR. You'll see. (*He turns to Hans*) Hans, what have you got in your pocket?

HANS. Nothing, so far as I know.

CASTOR. Would you mind putting your hand into your pocket and showing the King what is there?

HANS. Why, of course. There's nothing, I told you. (*He puts his hand into his pocket, produces the snuff-box and looks at it in surprise*) But this is not mine.

CASTOR. Tell His Majesty what it is, Hans.

HANS. It appears to be a snuff-box, but I've never seen it bef . . .

CASTOR. Open it, Hans.

(HANS *opens the box*)

Now, if you will be so kind as to take a pinch of snuff and read aloud what it says inside the lid.

HANS. What if I refuse?

KING. I think you had better do as he says, Hans.

(HANS *takes a pinch of snuff, sneezes, then reads the words*)

HANS.   "Yesterday's is what it was,
                Tomorrow's is what it will be,
                Today's is what it is.
                What is it?"

VOICE (*off*) Flash, as they say.

(SCRATCH *dives under the stool. The* KING *hides behind Castor.* MRS CRABTREE *hides behind Senna*)

Here is the very latest bit of gossip from the royal palace, over-heard from an unimpeachable source. Arch-Dowser Hypatia Crabtree is hot on the brimstone trail, ably assisted by her nephew, the redoubtable Euripides Scratch. The King, I'm told . . .

KING. That will do.

VOICE (*off*) Certainly, Your Majesty.

(HANS *snaps the box shut.* SCRATCH, *the* KING *and* MRS CRAB-TREE *come out of hiding.* MRS CRABTREE *moves down* R)

KING. Well, I don't think we need look any further for the source of our troubles. Master Hans, you will consider yourself under arrest for practising magic without a licence.
HANS. But, Your Majesty, please give me a hearing . . .
KING. That's enough. No more. Not another word.

(CASTOR *crosses above the others to* R *of Mrs Crabtree*)

Mrs Crabtree, I must congratulate you on a most successful piece of dowsing.
MRS CRABTREE. I only do my duty by society, King Rufus.
KING (*crossing to Mrs Crabtree*) Of course. But we are not yet out of the wood.

(SENNA *and* SCRATCH *join the King, Mrs Crabtree and Castor down* R)

We still have to find means of inducing this misguided young man to release his despicable hold on the Princess.
MRS CRABTREE. The ducking-stool is the only really effective method, I find.

(*The* PRINCESS, *unnoticed by the others, slowly rises and exits by the french windows up* C)

KING. Let us not be too hasty, Mrs Crabtree. We must first of all give Hans the opportunity of releasing the Princess from the spell and restoring her memory.

(SCRATCH *sees the Princess has gone, moves up* C, *looks under the couch and then out of the window*)

If he is willing to do this, perhaps we can mitigate the punishment somewhat. After all, we must remember that we are to some extent still in his hands. I should never forgive myself if . . .
SCRATCH (*moving below the couch*) Your Majesty!
KING. Don't interrupt, Scratch.
SCRATCH. But, Your Majesty, she's gone.
KING (*crossing to* L *of Scratch*) What's that? Who has?

(MRS CRABTREE *moves to* R *of the couch.* CASTOR *goes up* R. SENNA *crosses to* L *of the King*)

SCRATCH. The Princess! She's disappeared!
KING. Bless my soul, why didn't you stop her, Scratch?
SCRATCH. I never saw her go.
KING. Well, you should have. What do you think I pay you for?
SCRATCH. But I wasn't looking. I just turned round and there she wasn't.
KING. Well, don't stand there—go and look. The window's open—she must have gone that way.

(SCRATCH *hurries to the window up* C)

CASTOR—(*he indicates Hans*) keep an eye on this fellow till I get back. You help him, Senna. And don't let him out of your sight. (*He moves to the window and pushes Scratch aside*) Out of my way, Scratch.

(SCRATCH *falls on to the couch*)

You wouldn't see her if she was right under your nose.

MRS CRABTREE. Wait!

KING. Not now, Mrs C.

MRS CRABTREE. The hazel twig will find her. Wait! (*She touches the couch with the twig, and stands holding it in the approved manner*) Steady. Wait for it. The influence is there. I know it's there. (*The twig twitches*) I've got it! We're off! Follow me—follow the dowsing rod.

(MRS CRABTREE *whirls round twice in a circle, then, with cape flying, shoots off up* C)

(*Off*) The hunt is up! Follow me! Follow the dowsing rod.

(*The* KING *hurriedly follows Mrs Crabtree off.*
    SCRATCH *follows the* King *off.* HANS *starts to follow, but* CASTOR *and* SENNA *get to the window first and stand in his way*)

CASTOR. Oh, no, you don't. You stay here, you—you unqualified quack.

(HANS *looks round and then crosses towards the exit down* R)

(*He runs down* R *and bars the way*) It's no use trying to get away.

(SENNA *moves to* L *of Hans*)

HANS. But the Princess is in danger. We can't stand by and do nothing whilst the Princess may be lost. There's no telling what may happen to her.

SENNA. You must allow us, her official physicians, to be the best judges of that. The King will find her, if Crabtree doesn't.

CASTOR. Quite. Now, kindly sit down where we can keep an eye on you.

(CASTOR *and* SENNA *escort* HANS *to the couch*)

HANS. But the Princess . . .

CASTOR. Sit down, sir.

(HANS *sits on the couch*)

HANS. I don't know what you hope to gain by all this. You are simply making things worse for yourselves by persecuting me.

CASTOR (*sitting* R *of Hans on the couch*) I don't think so. You see, we know who is causing the Princess's illness.

HANS. Well, who is it?

CASTOR. Ah, that would be telling.

SENNA (*sitting* L *of Hans on the couch*) And we don't propose to tell until you are safely out of the way and unable to take credit for it.

HANS. I see. Pretty ornaments to the medical profession, I must say.

CASTOR. At least we are qualified in it.

(HANS *rises.* CASTOR *and* SENNA *grab* HANS *by the shoulders and reseat him*)

HANS. Knowing who bewitched the Princess doesn't get you very much further, either. How will you induce that person to release her from it?

CASTOR. What for?

HANS. What do you mean?

SENNA. The longer the Princess remains unchanged, the longer our bills for her treatment.

HANS. You mean you . . . ?

CASTOR }
SENNA }(*together*) Yes.

HANS. That's just about the lowest admission I've ever heard anyone make.

CASTOR. That is a matter of opinion. And whilst we are waiting I should be glad if you would hand over our property.

HANS. What property?

CASTOR. The snuff-box. Hand it over.

HANS. What if I refuse?

CASTOR. Senna, this young man is beginning to irritate. What do you suggest we ought to do?

SENNA. Neutralize him.

CASTOR. I think we should render him unconscious.

(SENNA *rises, removes a decorative cord from the couch and suddenly throws it over Hans' body and upper arms*)

HANS. Oh, you . . . !

CASTOR (*rising*) Now, hand over the snuff-box.

HANS. Come and get it.

CASTOR. Very well, if you're determined to be difficult . . . (*He moves towards Hans*)

(HANS *allows* CASTOR *to get within range, then suddenly lifts both feet to Castor's chest and knocks him backwards. He then lunges forward, pulling* SENNA *across the couch. There ensues a most undignified scramble, none of the three of them knowing much in the way of close combat, resulting in* HANS *being with difficulty overpowered by the other two, tied up and seated on the couch.* SENNA *takes a handkerchief from his pocket*)

SENNA (*gagging Hans*) Oh, Castor! Never ask me to do any-thing like that again. I'm black and blue all over.
CASTOR (*exhausted*) Nonsense! I—as—I could go the same again with one hand tied behind me. (*He collapses at the knees with a long sigh*) Ahhh! Get the snuff-box.

(SENNA *takes the snuff-box from Hans' pocket*)

(*He totters to his feet*) I need a cup of hot sweet tea. First degree shock—I can feel it coming on. (*He shivers and trembles violently*)
SENNA (*moving to Castor*) Castor, you look awful. Shall I send for the doctor?
CASTOR. Don't be stupid, Senna—you are one.
SENNA. Am I?

(SENNA *takes* CASTOR'S *arm and leads him towards the arch up* L. *The* GOBBIN *enters up* L)

GOBBIN. Hello. (*He grins*)
CASTOR (*clutching Senna in alarm*) Senna, what's that?
SENNA. It—it's a person—I think.
CASTOR. Tell him we don't want anything.
GOBBIN (*leering horribly*) Hello.
CASTOR (*in alarm*) Oh, my goodness!

(CASTOR *and* SENNA *sheer away from the* GOBBIN *who lumbers after them, making hideous faces.*
CASTOR *and* SENNA *gather speed as he follows them and flee through the french windows up* C)

GOBBIN (*grinning*) They don't like gobbins, do they?

(HANS *makes muffled noises under his gag*)

(*He crosses and sits beside Hans*) Hello. How've you gone on?

(HANS *struggles and mutters*)

Eh? What? I beg your pardon?

(HANS *mumbles*)

I can't tell what you're talking about.

(HANS' *efforts become frantic*)

(*He rises*) I'll come back when you've a bit more time. I'll like to know how you went on. (*He moves to the window, tripping over Hans' feet as he goes*) Ta-ra! (*He waves and grins*)

(HANS *makes as much effort as he can, stamping his feet on the ground*)

I wonder if he wants anything. I'll ask him. (*He moves to Hans and shouts in his ear, mouthing the words*) Do you want anything?

(HANS *redoubles his efforts to make the Gobbin understand*)

How can you talk to anybody with that thing in your mouth? (*He removes the gag*)

HANS. Gob, for Heaven's sake! Get me out of this rope.

GOBBIN. Don't you like it? I thought you'd done it on purpose. (*He unties the rope*)

HANS. I thought you were never going to get around to it, Gob. Couldn't you see I wanted help?

GOBBIN. Well, don't sauce me like that. I'm only a Gobbin.

HANS. I didn't mean it, Gob—I'm very grateful. We're still friends, eh?

GOBBIN. Of course.

HANS. Now, I've got to get out of here and find the Princess. (*He moves to the window up* C)

GOBBIN. Well, give her my love. Ta-ra.

(HANS *exits up* C)

(*To the audience*) Ee, I'm a proper gobbin, me.

CURTAIN

ACT II

SCENE I

SCENE—*The Forest.*
*The window and arch wings are removed, and the tree cut is now backed
by the closing of the upstage gauze* TABS *on which there is a tree design.
There is a tree up* LC, *a log for a seat down* C *and a small length of
fencing down* L.

When the CURTAIN *rises, the stage is empty. After a moment,* DAISY,
in great excitement, enters hurriedly up R.

DAISY (*circling the stage*) Oops, Daisy! Daisy's on the run. One,
two, three, they can't catch me. Oh, such a run for their money.
Whoops and tiddy-fol-lol, girls, let me get me breath for a minute.
(*She sits on the log* C *and vigorously fans herself with a corner of her shawl*)
Oh, dear—oh, dear—oh, dear! "Age cannot wither her", as the
poet says, but, my word, he's doing his best. Daisy ain't as young
as she was.

MRS CRABTREE (*off; calling*) Rally! Rally! Rally! Rally!
Follow me. Crabtree never fails.

DAISY (*rising*) Harden me arteries. They're after me yet.
Heel and toe, here we go; oh, my witchdom for a broomstick.
"Fly farther off", as the poet says, "there is no tarradiddle here".
A bane on Mrs Crabtree. (*She is capering off, but stops suddenly*)
Wait! No! That isn't the way, Daisy. Crabtree must be foiled.
Crabtree is formidable, but Daisy is formidabbler. Whoops! They
shall not pass. (*She dives a hand into her capacious pocket and produces
a red herring*) "A little red herring said to me, 'boot and saddle and
off to sea.' "

MRS CRABTREE (*off*) Rally! Rally!

DAISY. Rally, rally, I reply. (*She trails the herring round in a
circle on the ground, then nips behind the tree to watch*) Neat and tidy,
fish on Friday. Oh, Daisy's artful.

MRS CRABTREE (*off*) Follow the hazel twig.

(MRS CRABTREE *enters up* R, *hot and flustered, the hazel twig
rampant*)

(*As she enters and comes down* C) We're getting warmer, Euripides.
Follow the dowsing rod.

(*The* KING *enters up* R.
SCRATCH, *puffing and blowing, follows the King on*)

KING (*moving down* RC) Stop!

(MRS CRABTREE *stops*)

Mrs Crabtree, I cannot and will not go another step farther. This confounded mumbo-jumbo of yours is getting us nowhere.

MRS CRABTREE. Oh, but it is. It is. Look at the rod. I can hardly hold it. We're almost there, I'm sure of it.

KING. Oh, very well. I'm almost past feeling, anyway.

(MRS CRABTREE *continues. The twig pulls her to one side of the stage, then jerks uncertainly from side to side*)

MRS CRABTREE. There's—there's something wrong. A cross-influence is confusing the rod. Oh!

(*The last cry is rather desperate, as the twig drags her smartly off again, to follow the circle Daisy made with the herring.* MRS CRABTREE *tears round, the* KING *and* SCRATCH *dully following. Finally she spirals round into* C *and stops. As she looks in dismay at the twig, it snaps in two with a loud crack*)

(*Horrified*) Oh!

KING. Crabtree always gets her witch, eh?

(*The* KING *and* SCRATCH *sit on the log*)

MRS CRABTREE (*moving* LC) This is most frustrating. I've never been so close to the kill, and then for this to happen. What *will* Your Majesty think of me?

SCRATCH (*his idol shattered*) Oh, Auntie!

MRS CRABTREE. I don't understand it. Just when the trail was so fresh, and this was my very best dowsing-rod, too.

KING (*rising*) Well, I suppose all we can do now is to return to the palace. Come, Scratch.

(SCRATCH *rises*)

SCRATCH (*with a reproachful look at Mrs Crabtree*) Yes, Your Majesty.

(MRS CRABTREE *hangs her head. The* KING *moves up* C, *then looks uncertainly about him*)

KING. Er—Scratch.

SCRATCH. Sir?

KING (*pointing* R *and* L) Did we come that way or that way?

SCRATCH. I don't know. (*He points down* L) This way, wasn't it?

KING. Don't ask me, I'm asking *you*.

SCRATCH. And I'm telling you I don't know.

KING. Don't use that tone with me, Scratch.

SCRATCH. I wasn't using a tone.

KING. Yes, you were.

Scratch. No, I wasn't.
King. I said you were.
Scratch. Oh, all right, I'm sorry.
King. That's better.
Scratch. You always blame things on me.
King (*moving down* c) That will do. And don't let's quarrel, whatever we do.

(Mrs Crabtree *moves* l *of the King,* Scratch *to* r *of him*)

If, as I strongly suspect, we are lost in this forest . . .
Scratch. Lost?
King. I'm afraid so. And, as I say, *if* we are, the only way we shall get ourselves out of it is by being nice and friendly with each other, and not snapping each other's heads off. Mrs Crabtree.
Mrs Crabtree (*humbly*) Yes?
King. Do *you* know where we are?
Mrs Crabtree. I'm afraid I don't. I just follow the scent regardless. I have little sense of direction, I fear.
King. Just as I thought. Then we *are* lost.

(*There is a short silence, then* Scratch *kneels and begins to sniff as though he were going to cry*)

(*He looks at Scratch*) Scratch?
Scratch (*miserably*) Yes?
King. Are you crying?
Scratch (*with a sniff*) No.
King. You are.
Scratch. I'm not.
King. Yes, you are. And you mustn't. *I'm* not crying.

(Scratch *sniffs*)

Your Aunt Thingummy isn't crying.

(Scratch *sniffs*)

And so *you* mustn't cry.
Scratch (*with a wail*) But we're lost!
King (*moving a little up* c) Now, that's quite enough. I can't imagine what you're crying *for*. It isn't as if you were alone. I'm with you—your Aunt Thingummy's with you—so what on earth is there to be afraid of? Do you expect something to jump out of the forest and bite you or something?

(*Rumbling noises are heard off.* Mrs Crabtree *moves to* l *of the King*)

Scratch. Yes.
King. Well, it won't. If anyone is to be bitten it will be Mrs
c

CRABTREE. Now, just try to take your mind off it, and think of other things—nice things.

SCRATCH. I—I'll try.

KING. Thank Heaven for that!

SCRATCH (*rising and moving* R *of the King*) Will you—(*he sniffs*) will you tell me a story?

KING. I certainly will not tell you a story.

SCRATCH. I should feel much better if you would.

(*The* KING *sees* SCRATCH'S *lugubrious face looking at him*)

KING. Oh, all right, I—I'll see if I can remember something.

SCRATCH. Thank you.

(*The* KING *sits on the log.* SCRATCH *sits* R *of him,* MRS CRAB-TREE *sits* L *of him. There is a pause while the* KING *thinks.* DAISY, *unseen by the others, tiptoes from behind the tree and creeps behind the trio on the log. She is armed with a butterfly net*)

KING. Are you sitting comfortably?

SCRATCH. Yes.

KING. Then I will begin.

DAISY (*in a nervous whisper*) Gently does it, Daisy dear. Whoops, careful!

KING. Once upon a time . . .

(DAISY *makes three snatches with the net in the air behind their heads. Their expressions go blank at once*)

DAISY (*as she snatches*) Snip, snap, snip! Three at a go. Daisy, you're a caution! (*She capers* RC, *takes three invisible handfuls out of the net, and pops them into her pocket*) Oh, lovely, lovely, lovely. Three beautiful memories to add to Daisy's priceless collection. (*She capers down* R) With a fal lal la and a derry down day. Oh, my Aunt Eliza. Royal reminiscences, secretarial secrets, and the daring doings of a dowser. Oh, sensational scavenging. Unprecedented pickings. What a time Daisy will have with herself, rummaging through this little heap of souvenirs. Ah, but wait! What? (*She moves behind the others*) Yes, what shall we do with the bodies? Turn them adrift, of course. Set them at liberty. "Liberty, Freedom—tyranny is dead", said the Bard, and who shall say him nay. Not Daisy, not on your life. (*She moves* C) Come, Euripides. (*She takes Scratch by the hand*)

(SCRATCH *rises and looks blankly at Daisy*)

SCRATCH. Who are you?

DAISY. What's more to the point is who are *you?*

SCRATCH. Me? I think . . . I don't know who I am.

DAISY. Then why worry about me, little man? What can you recollect about yourself? H'm?

Scratch (*after a pause*) Nothing. (*He pauses*) I can remember nothing.

Daisy. That's it! Not nothing, not nobody, nohow. Oh, clever Daisy. Then you'd better start looking for yourself, hadn't you? (*She turns him round*) Off you go, Euripides. (*She gives him a push*)

(Scratch *sets off vaguely into the forest and exits down* l)

(*She crosses to* l *of Mrs Crabtree*) You there!

Mrs Crabtree. Do you mean me?

Daisy. Yes, you. What are you doing here?

Mrs Crabtree. What business is that of yours?

Daisy (*moving down* l) Oh, la la! Crabtree sauce, forsooth. (*She returns and sits* l *of Mrs Crabtree on the log*)

Mrs Crabtree. If you must know, I'm—well, I'm—sitting in the forest with—(*she looks at the King*) a perfect stranger.

Daisy. Well, don't you think you'd better stop it?

Mrs Crabtree (*rising*) Yes, I—I suppose I better had. (*She looks about her, bewildered*) Strange, I can't for the life of me remember how I came to be here, or who I am, or even what my name is.

(Mrs Crabtree *wanders up* r *and exits.* Daisy *moves along the log, sits beside the King and rests her head on his shoulder*)

King (*coming to his senses somewhat*) My good woman!

Daisy (*sitting up*) Oh, my elastic stockings! Daisy's never been called "good" before. Yes, my good man?

King. I'm a little confused as to where I am. Can you possibly help me to find my way back to—to . . . Bless my soul, I don't even know where I'm going.

Daisy. Nor where you've been?

King. Nor where I've been.

Daisy. Nor who you are nor where you are nor what you are not whether it's half past six or Pancake Thursday? Eh? Do you? Is it?

King. Yes. No. *Please*, please, I'm so confused, I—I can't think . . .

Daisy (*rising and moving to* l *of the log*) Then don't.

(*The* King *rises and moves to* r *of the log*)

Thinking never did anybody any good, you know. I never think.

(*They bow to each other*)

I just act according to impulse. (*She moves to the* King, *grabs him and dances around with him*) And what impulses Daisy does get.

(Daisy *releases the King, crosses and exits down* l, *leaving the* King *utterly bewildered*)

KING (*crossing to* L) Oh, no—please come back just for a moment. I—I—I . . . (*He turns uncertainly and goes up* L)

(*The* PRINCESS *enters down* L. *The* KING *turns and crosses to* RC)

(*He sees the Princess. Politely*) Good afternoon. (*He moves* R, *stops, and turns, puzzled, to look at the Princess*)

(*The* PRINCESS *looks at the King, puzzled, and shakes her head. The* KING *shakes his head and exits down* R. *The* PRINCESS *starts to follow the King, then hesitates and moves up* C)

PRINCESS. If only I could remember—if only I could . . .

(HANS *enters down* L)

HANS. Princess! (*He runs to her*) Are you all right? Thank goodness I've found you.

PRINCESS. Yes, I think so. I seem to know you. I've seen you somewhere before.

HANS. Of course you have. In the palace.

PRINCESS. Yes. You are a doctor.

HANS. In a way, I am. Tell me, why did you run away?

PRINCESS. Run away? Did I?

HANS. Yes, don't you remember? We were all talking and you just got up and went out. Why?

PRINCESS (*moving down* C) I think—I think I wanted to find someone.

HANS. And did you?

PRINCESS. Not yet.

HANS. Well, don't try to think any more. (*He leads the Princess to the log*) Just rest, and presently we'll go back to your father.

PRINCESS (*sitting on the log*) What is your name?

HANS. Hans.

PRINCESS. Hans. You seem to understand me. I only wish I could understand myself. If only I could remember things . . .

HANS. Now, don't worry. (*He sits* L *of the Princess on the log*) Everything will turn out all right, you'll see.

PRINCESS. Of course. We don't have to go back *just* yet, do we?

HANS. Not if you don't want to.

PRINCESS. It's nice in the forest. As I was walking through it just now, I—it was like discovering it for the first time. I suppose I've seen it before, but not remembering it, it all seems so fresh and new—how the sunlight makes moving patterns on the ground, and how if you stand quite still and don't breathe there's a kind of silence you don't find anywhere else—a silence you can almost hear. And then suddenly from nowhere at all there's a squirrel sitting right in front of you, licking its whiskers and paying no attention to you at all. You see, I can remember some things—recent things.

HANS. Of course you can. It will all come back to you presently.

PRINCESS (*rising*) I hope so. (*She moves down* R *and turns*) Hans.
HANS. Yes, Princess?
PRINCESS. If I don't ever get my memory back . . .
HANS (*rising*) You mustn't say things like that.
PRINCESS. No, but if I don't . . .
HANS. Well?
PRINCESS. Well, I don't think I should mind quite so much as long as I had someone—someone like you—with me.
HANS (*moving to the Princess and taking her hands*) I can think of nothing better than to be with you all the time, but . . .
PRINCESS. But what?
HANS. Well, you see, you are a princess, a king's daughter, very grand and important, and I—I'm nobody at all.
PRINCESS. I don't feel grand and important and you're—(*she crosses to* C *and turns to him*) you're Hans and you're very important to me. Promise you'll stay with me, Hans.
HANS. I'll stay with you.
PRINCESS (*sitting on the log*) I think I'm happy now—happier than I've been for a long time.
HANS. Perhaps we ought to be starting back, now. (*He moves to the Princess*) The forest is large, and I'm not altogether sure of the way.
PRINCESS. Supposing we couldn't find our way out; then we should always be together, shouldn't we? That would be wonderful, to make the forest our home, and never go back to where it matters about being somebody or nobody.

(SYLVESTER *enters nonchalantly up* L. *He is exquisitely, even ostentatiously dressed and looks quite out of place in such rural surroundings. One elegant hand is lightly holding the ends of two pink ribbons, the other ends of which are out of sight in the wings. For all that, he is only a swineherd*)

Here, it doesn't matter at all who you are.
SYLVESTER. Ah, but it does. (*He stands by the tree up* LC)

(HANS *and the* PRINCESS, *startled, rise and turn to Sylvester*)

HANS. Where did you spring from? (*He moves* R *of the log*)

(*The* PRINCESS *moves down* R *of Hans*)

SYLVESTER. Spring is hardly the word. I never do anything so vigorous if I can help it. You say it doesn't matter in the forest who you are; let me inform you it matters a great deal. Take me, for instance. I am quite definitely Somebody in these parts.
HANS. Would it be very much out of place to ask who you are?
SYLVESTER. Not at all. I can see you are a stranger in the forest. My name is Sylvester.
HANS. How do you do? My name is Hans. I am a student.
SYLVESTER. Of what?

HANS. Medicine. And this is my patient, the Princess.
SYLVESTER. Princess who?
HANS. *The* Princess. The King's daughter.
SYLVESTER (*moving down* L *of the log*) Ah. (*To the Princess*) How do you do?
PRINCESS. How do you do?
SYLVESTER. What king?
HANS. King Rufus, of course.
SYLVESTER. Why "of course"? *I* never heard of him.
HANS. But you must be one of his subjects.
SYLVESTER. Not in the least. I owe allegiance only to the Queen of the Forest, whom I serve.
HANS. Well, *I* never heard of her, so that makes us even.
SYLVESTER (*sitting on the log*) Even, perhaps; equal, never.
HANS. Look, what *are* you, really?
SYLVESTER. What am I? I am Swineherd to the Queen.
HANS. A swineherd? Is *that* all?
SYLVESTER. *All?* It is a very great deal, I assure you. There are swine and swine, you know. Swineherd to the Queen is an office of some moment.
HANS. Where are your swine, then?
SYLVESTER. On the other end of these ribbons. Would you care to meet them?
HANS. I can hardly wait.

(SYLVESTER *hauls on the ribbons.*

HANK *and* HUNK *trot on* L, *cross and stand one each side of the Princess. They have lace collars and blue bows on their tails*)

SYLVESTER. Allow me to introduce Hank and Hunk, the Queen's Swine. (*To Hank and Hunk*) Say, "How do you do?" to the lady and gentleman.
HANK (*bobbing to the Princess*) Hoink!
HUNK (*bobbing to the Princess*) Hoink, hoink!
PRINCESS. How do you do? They really are rather sweet.
SYLVESTER. They are highly accomplished animals, ma'am, and terribly well bred.
PRINCESS. But won't their collars get dirty, grubbing about in the forest?

(HANK *and* HUNK *look horrified and retreat down* R)

SYLVESTER. Grubbing about? They never do that.
HANK (*deprecatingly*) Hoink!
HUNK (*loftily*) Hoink, hoink, hoink!

(HANK *and* HUNK *cross above the others to* L *of Sylvester*)

SYLVESTER. Hunk is the talkative one. No, you see, they don't feed in the forest. But they like to take a little stroll now and then, when the weather is fine. If it isn't, they continue their lessons.

PRINCESS. Lessons? Pigs taking lessons?

SYLVESTER. And why not?

PRINCESS. But what do they learn?

SYLVESTER (*rising and crossing to* L) Oh, dancing, fencing, water-colours; you know the sort of thing. Their gavotte is quite something.

(HANK *and* HUNK *display well-bred excitement at the mention of the gavotte, hoinking and clapping their trotters*)

There! I shouldn't have mentioned it. They won't be satisfied now until they've given you a demonstration. Stop it, you little pigs.

(HANK *and* HUNK *subside*)

(*To the Princess*) Do you mind very much? They do like to show off, I'm afraid.

PRINCESS (*sitting on the log*) Oh, do let them.

SYLVESTER. I'll just loosen their collars first. (*He removes the ribbons*)

(HANK *and* HUNK *take their places for the gavotte*)

(*He beats time and counts*) And——

(*Music is heard.* HANK *and* HUNK *dance*)

—one and two and three and point; one and two and three and point; one and two and . . .

(SYLVESTER, *during the dance, crosses above the log to* L *of Hans.* HANK *and* HUNK, *when they have finished their dance, bow to each other, then jump up and down, clapping their trotters and hoinking*)

No, you mustn't go through it again.

(HANK *and* HUNK *move to Sylvester and hoink the more*)

No, I said, and that's final.

(HANK *and* HUNK *turn their backs*)

(*To Hans*) It doesn't do to give way to them too much.

PRINCESS. They are very clever, but why do they get such special treatment? After all, they are only pigs.

SYLVESTER (*sitting* R *of the Princess on the log*) Now, that's where you are mistaken, ma'am. They are very special pigs, in fact, magic pigs. You don't imagine the Queen of the Forest would have anything ordinary, do you?

HANS (*crossing to Hank and Hunk*) *Magic* pigs, eh? *We* could do with a little magic just now.

HANK⎫
HUNK⎭(*together*) Hoink!

SYLVESTER. Really? But why ever didn't you say? (*He strikes a*

pose) I'm magic, too, you know—a sort of Fairy Swineherd you might call me. (*He turns to the Princess*) It's a very enchanted locality, taking it all round. What exactly is the trouble?
HANS. Well, it's the Princess, mainly. Her memory has been stolen—she's bewitched.
SYLVESTER. No!
HANS. Yes, indeed.
SYLVESTER. Well, I never! You know who has it, of course?
HANS. That's it, you see, we don't. (*He moves above the log*)
SYLVESTER (*leaning down to the Princess*) Oh, that makes it *very* awkward.
PRINCESS. But we do—at least, I do.
HANS. But you never told anybody you knew who it was.
PRINCESS. Perhaps nobody thought of asking me.
HANS. Who is it, then?
PRINCESS. It's somebody called Daisy.
HANS. Daisy?
PRINCESS. Yes, I can't recall her other name.

(HANK *and* HUNK *jump about and hoink*)

SYLVESTER. Just a minute. I think they know.

(HANK *and* HUNK *move to Sylvester and clamour for attention, with much hoinking and pointing*)

Oh, please, please. Don't both hoink at once. One at a time, now.

(HANK *and* HUNK *subside a little, and an elaborate conversation ensues as they hoink alternately, interspersed with* SYLVESTER'S *comments*)

Yes . . . Yes . . . Over there . . . I see . . . *Is* she? . . . *Does* she? . . . She *didn't!* . . . What? . . . Yes . . . All right, I've got it . . . I've got it. (*He rises and pushes them down* R) All *right*, I said. (*To the Princess*) Really there's no stopping them once they start.
PRINCESS. What did they say?
SYLVESTER. Well, it seems that over the other side of the forest lives a witch called—Daisy Crockett or Crewcut or something . . .
HUNK. *Hoink-hoink!*
SYLVESTER. What? "Crowfoot", that's it—Crowfoot. Well now, she is the one, and from what they say she is *the* most powerful witch ever. And believe me, they know.
HANK. Hoink!

(*The* PRINCESS *rises and moves down* LC. HANS *moves to the Princess*)

SYLVESTER. It appears she steals people's memories and keeps them in little glass bottles, all neatly labelled like medicine.
PRINCESS. But what for?

Sylvester. Now, how can you expect pigs to know that?
Hank ⎱ *(together)* Hoink!
Hunk ⎰
Hans. Did they tell you any more?
Sylvester. Oh, lots. They could write a book about Daisy—
if they could write, that is.
Hans. Can't they?
Sylvester *(sitting on the log)* Of course not—they're not old
enough.

(Hank *and* Hunk *cross and stand behind Sylvester*)

Hans. I meant did they tell you anything useful to *us*—like
how to get to where Daisy lives, for instance?
Sylvester. Oh, yes; I can tell you that. Now, you go through
this clump of bushes . . . Er—by the way, do you know this forest
at all?
Hans. I'm afraid not.
Sylvester. Ah, well, that makes a difference. Look, do you
see that . . . ? No, you can't see it from here. *(He rises)* I think
the only thing for it is to take you there.
Hans. That's most kind of you, but we don't want to put you
out . . .
Sylvester. Oh, it's all right. It's only a *few* miles out of our
way. *(He fixes the ribbons to Hank and Hunk)*

(Hans *and the* Princess *move up* c)

I'll just put their ribbons on again, so they don't catch cold.
They're delicate, you know. Inbreeding, I expect. There, now.
If you'll kindly follow me.

(Sylvester *is starting to lead the way, when a woman's voice,
very musical, is heard calling*)

Queen *(off; calling)* Syl-vest-er!
Sylvester. Oh, dear, that's rather spoilt it, I'm afraid. I
shan't be able to go with you after all.
Queen *(off; calling)* Syl-vest-er!
Sylvester *(calling)* Com-ing. *(To Hans)* I shall have to go.
Princess. Whose was the voice?
Sylvester. That's the Queen—the Queen of the Forest, you
know.
Princess. Where is she?
Sylvester. Actually, she's invisible. We are, too, normally,
only it happens to be Leap Year. Now, look, what you'd better
do is to strike east—keep the sun on your right all the time. You
won't go far wrong, and I'll try and catch you up later. How's
that?

(Hans *and the* Princess *cross down* r *and turn*)

HANS. That's fine, only—you won't forget, will you?
SYLVESTER. I won't forget. 'Bye now. (*To Hank and Hunk*)
Wave to the lady and gentleman. 'Bye.

(HANK *and* HUNK *wave.*
HANS *and the* PRINCESS *wave in reply and exit down* R)

What a dull couple. Nice, though, in their way.

(SYLVESTER *leads* HANK *and* HUNK *off down* L.
DAISY, *highly delighted with herself, enters up* L)

DAISY. Interesting. Very very interesting. And they think Daisy
doesn't know. (*She moves down* C) But they don't know Daisy.
Not on your sweet life, they don't. (*She crosses and looks off down* R)
There they go, tripping through the trees, all on their way to
call on Daisy in Daisy's little cottage. (*She moves* C) Ah, but Daisy
won't be there, and neither will Daisy's little cottage. "And why?"
did you say? "Ah, why, ah, why," cried the rhubarb pie, "why
was I baked so long?" Because Daisy is going to flit—to move
house—every last brick of it. Oh, elusive little Daisy. (*She circles* R
and goes up C) Where would be a suitable spot to which to trans-
late me little menage? Where's the last place they would look for
me? Why here, of course. A delightful, secluded spot and no
ground rent. And therefore and forthwith and without more ado
—a spell. (*She recites*)
"Hey diddle diddle, the ends and the middle,
The kettle, the pot and the broom,
Lift and take it and—careful don't break it,
And set it down there with a boom,
Set it down there with a boom, for Daisy,
Set it down there with a *boom*."

(*There is a puff of smoke and a clap of thunder as the cottage
appears* R. *The cottage is mounted on a truck and is run in on tracks
above the middle wing* R. *It is like Teapot Hall, all roof and no wall,
and quite as crazy as its owners in its lineaments. It has a tiny door* R
and a small window L. *Over the door is a neat little notice in poker-
work:* "En-dor Cottage. Potions while you wait")

There we are. Now, just to make sure the fire's in.

(DAISY *goes into the cottage and shuts the door. Smoke begins to
come out of the chimney.*
DAISY *pops out again*)

Botheration! Of course I *would* forget to charm the firewood here
as well as the fire. That means I'll have to collect some more.
Double botheration!

(DAISY *trots off up* L.
CASTOR *enters cautiously down* R)

CASTOR (*over his shoulder*)   Sh! Don't make so much noise, Senna.

(SENNA *enters down* R)

Where's your woodcraft!

SENNA. I can't help it. I hate forests, anyway. They're too damp. My feet are all wet.

CASTOR. They're not the only part of you that's all wet.

SENNA (*moving below Castor to* C)   I think I'm getting pneumonia. (*He coughs*) I'm sure I'm getting it. I'm going back.

CASTOR (*restraining Senna*)   Senna, we've got to find the Princess's memory, and we've got to find it first. Now, pull yourself together.

SENNA. You wouldn't have a couple of aspirins on you, I suppose?

CASTOR. No, I wouldn't.

SENNA. You might at least take my temperature.

CASTOR. I've no thermometer.

SENNA. Or my pulse. Take my hand.

CASTOR. No. I've no watch.

SENNA. You're just being beastly to me. (*He stamps on Castor's foot*)

CASTOR. Oh, for heaven's sake! Look, you can't have pneumonia here. You must wait till we get home again, then you can have the doctor.

SENNA (*crossing to the cottage*)   Look, there's a cottage.

CASTOR. So there is. (*He moves to Senna*)

SENNA. They might have some aspirin. Shall I go and ask?

CASTOR. Wait! *This* is Daisy's cottage.

SENNA. Oh, Castor. Do you think so?

CASTOR (*moving* LC)   I'm sure, but we must be careful. Daisy's dangerous.

(SENNA *moves to Castor*)

You'd better go and see if she's in.

(SENNA *moves towards the cottage, then stops and returns to Castor*)

SENNA. Why me?

CASTOR. One of us has to go. Besides, you're more expendable.

SENNA (*moving to* R *of the tree*)   You hate me. You just want to be rid of me.

CASTOR. Oh, all right, we'll both go. (*He moves towards the cottage*) Come on.

(SENNA *follows Castor*)

Peep through the window, first.

(*They creep to the window and look inside*)

SENNA. Can't see anybody. But look at all those bottles. A regular dispensary.

(*A slight cracking noise is heard off* L)

CASTOR. Sh! I can hear someone in the wood.

(DAISY's *voice is heard, singing*)

It's Daisy. Hide round the back, quick.

(CASTOR *and* SENNA *hide behind the cottage.*
DAISY *enters* L, *carrying a bundle of sticks which she deposits by the side of the cottage door*) .

DAISY. Poof! I'm puffed. What a trail for a little bit of kindling. (*She straightens up and sniffs the air*) That's rum! (*She moves down* R *and sniffs*) Very rum. Rum ti tum tum, an unusual hum. Mothballs? Eucalyptus? (*She crosses to* L) No, but equally clinical——

(SENNA *and* CASTOR *peer out*)

—equally finickal, antiseptically prophylactical. (*She turns*)

(SENNA *and* CASTOR *hide*)

Oh, what lovely long words Daisy does know. (*She crosses to* C) A fig for Roedean. Somebody nasty has been around. Well, they're not around now, so we'll forget 'em. (*She moves to the cottage*) Now, for a nice little cup of nettle tea.

(DAISY *picks up the wood and goes into the cottage. Smoke puffs out of the chimney.* CASTOR *and* SENNA *peep out, then cautiously approach the door, but hastily retreat behind the cottage as* DAISY *reappears carrying a stool with a cup of tea and a glass phial on it. She stops and switches her eyeballs to left and right suspiciously*)

What was that? (*She pauses*) Nothing—probably Lucy. Lucy Nation. (*She moves* C) She often plays little tricks on Daisy. But Daisy don't mind. She knows a trick or two herself. And here's one of her favourites. (*She sets the stool* C, *picks up the phial and cup of tea, settles herself comfortably on the stool, sips the tea, gazes into the phial and sighs*) Now for my daily gloat. People wonder why I steal memories. I steal them because—because—(*she sniffs in self-pity*) I never had no childhood—any childhood—born full-grown out of a thorn-bush when a flash of lightning struck it. Never played hopscotch like she's doing now—and she's so pretty. I might have been as pretty as that, you know—and as happy— happy as the day is long, I was—she was, I mean. Are they her memories or are they mine? Mine. They're mine, I say; all mine; happy, happy days so long ago. (*She suddenly shakes herself out of it*) Steady, Daisy—steady, girl; mustn't give way to sentiment too much—that way sanity lies, and who'd be sane, I'd like to know? Mustn't overdo it. (*She suddenly rises*) Oh, brambles and buttermilk! I've left the kettle on, burning its copper bottom out, wither it!

(Daisy *puts down the phial and exits hurriedly to the cottage, taking the teacup with her.* Castor *and* Senna *emerge at once, much excited*)

Castor. Did you hear what she was saying, Senna?

Senna. I heard it, but I didn't understand it. That woman only speaks one sensible word in three.

Castor. She meant . . . (*He sees the phial*) Look. She's left it behind.

Senna. Left what behind?

Castor. The phial with the Princess's memory.

Senna. Are you sure?

Castor. Of course. (*He picks up the phial*) Look for yourself. (*He gazes into the phial*) See, there's the Princess herself—but it's a long time ago. She must have been about fourteen.

Senna. Yes, yes; I see her. (*He moves to the log and sits*) I remember—it was the day she was given the white pony for her birthday.

Castor (*moving and sitting beside Senna on the log*) She's giving it sugar. Oh, that *was* a happy day for her.

(Daisy, *unseen by the other two, comes out of the cottage, carrying her butterfly net, and creeps up behind them*)

I remember it well—the King had sacked us twice that morning.

Daisy (*making two snatches with the net in the air above their heads*) Snip, snap.

(Senna *and* Castor *relapse into amnesia*)

Got 'em. Thought they'd get the better of Daisy, eh? Lovely, lovely! Always works, it does. I'll take that, thank you. (*She takes the phial from Castor's unresisting hand*) Phew! Nearly lost it that time, though. We'll have you back inside where it's safer.

(Daisy *bustles into the cottage and returns minus the phial and net, but carrying a bowl of onions and two knives*)

(*She crosses to Castor and Senna*) We must give you something to do. Can't have you idle, you know. And daily help is just what I've been short of. Oh, clever little Daisy. (*To Castor*) Here, you. What do you think I keep you for?

Castor. What? What did you say?

Daisy. Haven't forgotten who *I* am, by any chance, have you?

Castor. You? Why, yes, I . . .

Daisy. And who *you* are?

Castor. Who *am* I?

Daisy. You're the staff.

Senna. Staff?

DAISY. The lackeys, the scullions, the skivvies. Here. (*She thrusts the bowl at them*)
CASTOR (*taking the bowl*) What's this?
DAISY. Peel 'em.
SENNA. Peel them?
DAISY. Then slice 'em.
CASTOR. Slice them?
DAISY. Then make them into soup for my supper.
CASTOR ⎫
SENNA ⎭ (*together*) Soup?
DAISY. Soup. *Potage. Potage à l'oignon.* Delicious. Daisy's favourite dish. And sharps the word.

(CASTOR *and* SENNA *start to peel the onions*)

(*She crosses to the cottage*) Onion soup. Mmmmmm! I can hardly wait. (*She turns*) Beautiful soup!
CASTOR ⎫
SENNA ⎭ (*together*) Beautiful, beautiful, *beautiful soup!*

DAISY *goes into the cottage.* CASTOR *and* SENNA *continue peeling in silence. Very soon they begin to cry, softly at first, then loudly and unrestrainedly as—*

the downstage gauze TABS *close*

SCENE 2

SCENE—*Another part of the Forest.*
The scene is played in front of the downstage gauze TABS.

The PRINCESS *and* HANS *enter slowly* L, *hand in hand.* HANS *is talking, and for the moment they are oblivious of their surroundings. They cross to* C.

HANS. . . . and then we used to have wonderful holidays in the mountains. We used to swim and fish all day—the water was as clear as glass, so clear you could see the markings on the fish as they swam over the stones.
PRINCESS. It must be wonderful to remember all that—and to look back on it—whenever you want to.
HANS. Oh, I'm sorry, Princess. How clumsy I am to go rambling on about my memories, when you . . . Please forgive me.
PRINCESS. But there's nothing to forgive. It's very easy to listen to you, Hans. Easy for me, at least. Not remembering anything, I have nothing much to talk about, so I just listen. Hans——
HANS. Yes?

PRINCESS. —I don't want to be difficult, but do you really think we are going in the right direction?

HANS. Oh, I think so—wait a minute, though. Did Sylvester say to keep the sun on our right or on our left?

PRINCESS. Left, I think.

HANS. I thought he said right.

PRINCESS. This part of the forest is so gloomy it doesn't seem to be much help. You can't tell *where* the sun is.

(HANS *moves and looks anxiously around*)

Hans.

HANS. Yes?

PRINCESS. We're not lost again, are we?

HANS. No, no, of course not, only . . .

PRINCESS. Only what?

HANS. Well, there's something strange about this place. (*He crosses to* LC) Look—can you see, very faintly marked on the ground—a sort of outline.

PRINCESS (*moving* LC) The outline of a house.

HANS. Yes. Whatever sort of house it was, it's only recently been pulled down.

(SYLVESTER *enters hurriedly* L)

SYLVESTER. I'm terribly sorry I've been so long. (*He crosses to* C) It's the Queen, you know. One simply can't get away from her. She's a charming woman in her way, but possessive to a fault. Well, have you found it—the cottage, I mean?

PRINCESS. It doesn't seem to be here.

SYLVESTER. Not here? Oh, but it must be. I'm sure it was this morning. Hank and Hunk are never wrong.

HANS. Well, it isn't here now. It's as if the whole house had been lifted up and spirited away.

SYLVESTER. How simply maddening for you. That's witches, you see. You never can tell with them. So you're no nearer.

HANS. Not really. That Daisy is as difficult to pin down as a ferret. Well, what do we do now?

SYLVESTER. It's no use looking at me. There's no telling where she's got to.

HANS. What about the pigs? I'm sure they'd help us again if we asked them.

PRINCESS (*crossing to Sylvester*) Yes, where are they, Sylvester?

SYLVESTER. They're not very well, I'm afraid. The excitement, you know. In fact I've had to put them to bed with hot-water bottles. They hated it, but what could I do? (*He takes the Princess down* R) The Queen would never forgive me if they caught anything.

HANS. Sylvester, this Queen of yours . . .

SYLVESTER (*moving* RC) What about her?

HANS. Is she very powerful?

SYLVESTER. Oh, very. But difficult, *very* difficult.

HANS (*crossing to Sylvester*) Could she help us to find the Princess's memory?

SYLVESTER. Oh, there's no doubt she *could*—the point is, *would* she?

HANS. Well, would she?

SYLVESTER. Frankly—no. Not unless she were made to, and present company excepted, you know how difficult it is to make a woman do anything.

PRINCESS. Not even if we appealed to her sense of kindness?

SYLVESTER. She's very little of that, I find. Of course, you can always try.

HANS. Can you take me to her?

SYLVESTER (*leading Hans down* L) If you really want me to, but are you absolutely sure?

HANS. Absolutely. She seems to be our only hope at the moment. Is she far away?

SYLVESTER. She is and she isn't. She's everywhere and nowhere, if you see what I mean.

HANS. I'm afraid I don't.

SYLVESTER. Well, it's no use pressing the point. I'll show you her Grotto—that's where she lives. But just before I do—I must warn you that getting in is very much easier than getting out.

HANS. Why is that?

SYLVESTER. You'll see. (*He crosses to* C) You are quite positive you want to see the Queen?

HANS. Quite positive.

SYLVESTER. Well, don't say I didn't warn you. (*He turns his back to the audience, removes his hat and makes a sweeping bow. Formally*) Hans the Student demands . . .

PRINCESS (*interrupting and crossing to* C) May I not go in with you, Hans?

SYLVESTER (*leading the Princess down* R) I'm afraid that's quite out of the question, Princess. One at a time is the rule when the Queen gives audience.

HANS. Don't leave her alone in the forest, will you, Sylvester?

SYLVESTER. I won't. Look, you had better not hesitate too long. The Grotto has a habit of fading out of sight if you keep it waiting.

(HANS *crosses to* C)

PRINCESS. I—I'd rather you didn't go.

HANS. You needn't be afraid. Sylvester will stay with you.

PRINCESS (*crossing to Hans*) I don't mean that; I—I have a strange feeling of danger—a feeling I may never see you again.

HANS. But I'm only going to ask the Queen's help. If she refuses, we shall be no worse off than we are now. What harm can that do?

SYLVESTER (*crossing to* R *of the Princess*) I don't want to press you, but I don't think you'd better wait much longer, Hans. (*He leads the Princess down* R)
HANS. Look after her for me, won't you?

(SYLVESTER *moves* RC, *faces up stage and bows*)

SYLVESTER. Hans the Student demands audience of the Queen. (*To Hans*) Now, do be careful. Think hard before you answer her questions.

HANS *faces up stage. The gauze* TABS *open a little and* HANS *goes through as*——

the lights BLACK-OUT

SYLVESTER *and the* PRINCESS *exit down* R *in the* BLACK-OUT, *then the* LIGHTS *come up behind the gauze* TABS *on to the next scene.*

SCENE 3

SCENE—*The Queen of the Forest's Grotto.*
The upstage TABS *are open and there is a throne on the dais in the centre arch of the tree cut-cloth. The dais and the side arches are backed by human figures, apparently carved in stone. The Grotto's sombre splendour befits the Queen of the Forest.*

When the LIGHTS *come up, the downstage gauze* TABS *open.* HANS *looks round at the curious throne and the figures. For a moment he hesitates, then moves a little up* C. *As he does so, soft voices appear to emanate in varying tones from the statues.*

LIGHT VOICES (*off*) Hans—Hans—Hans . . .
DARK VOICES (*off*) Turn back—turn back—turn back . . .
HANS. Who are you? Why do you tell me to turn back?
LIGHT VOICES (*off*) She is cruel—cruel—cruel . . .
DARK VOICES (*off*) She is kind—kind—kind . . .
HANS. Who is? Who is?
LIGHT VOICES (*off*) She is ugly—ugly—ugly . . .
DARK VOICES (*off*) She is beautiful—beautiful—beautiful . . .
HANS (*moving up* C) But who? Who?
ALL VOICES (*off*) The Queen—the Queen—the Queen. Hans, turn back—run, Hans—run, Hans—she is cruel—cruel—kind, kind—ugly, ugly—beautiful, beautiful—she will turn you to stone—turn you to stone—turn you to stone . . .

(*The* VOICES *increase to a confused, insistent urgency until* HANS *turns bewildered in the centre of the room as though he were pressed from all sides, his hands over his ears. He goes up* R, *as though trying to find his way out. Suddenly the* Voices *cease, and a strain of music replaces them.*

The Queen of the Forest *enters down* l *and stands regarding Hans coldly. She is splendidly dressed in green and gold, and her face is partly hidden by a mask of gold.* Hans *turns, sees the Queen and takes his hands from his ears. The* Queen *crosses to* c, *goes up* c *to the dais, ascends it and turns. The* Voices *are heard*)

(*Very softly, and diminishing*) The Queen—the Queen—the Queen . . .

(*The* Voices *fade*)

QUEEN. The Princess Alicia is safe enough for the moment, Hans.

HANS (*moving* c) How did you know I was thinking of her?

QUEEN. The Queen of the Forest knows everything. The trees watch and the grass listens, and the wind tells me what they hear—(*she sits on the throne*) and what they see.

HANS. Were those the voices I heard?

QUEEN. Those were the voices of the Grotto. They are meaningless.

HANS. They seemed to be telling me to turn back, to run away.

QUEEN. There is no turning back now, Hans, and no running away. If you did not need my help you should not have come.

HANS (*kneeling*) I do need your help.

QUEEN. What do you want of me? Fame? Wealth? Honour?

HANS. I want nothing for myself.

QUEEN (*mockingly*) Noble and unselfish Hans. For whom, then?

HANS. For—for someone who is very near to me. For the Princess Alicia.

QUEEN. My help is rarely given, and not given easily. (*She rises*) You must be prepared to pay for it. (*She moves a little down* LC)

HANS (*rising*) I am a poor man, Your Majesty. But anything I can give I will give willingly to see the Princess restored to her former self.

QUEEN. Even your life, Hans? Would you give your life?

HANS. If it were the only thing I could give, yes, I would.

QUEEN. It may come to that; because those who ask for my help must first risk their lives to obtain it. (*She moves down* LC) Look around you. Those faces of stone were once the faces of living men. They asked for my help, but they failed in the tasks I set them to earn it.

(HANS *moves up* L, *looks at the statues, crosses and looks at the statues* R, *then turns to look at the Queen*)

Now you know the risk—do you still ask for my help?

HANS. I still ask it.

QUEEN. Very well. It is a simple task. If you can answer one question I shall put to you, and answer it correctly, I may not refuse your request. If you cannot answer it, you will turn instantly to stone. You understand?

HANS. I understand. (*He moves up* LC)

(*The* QUEEN *moves down* R, *turns and faces Hans*)

QUEEN. Look at me, Hans. Look at the mask of gold which hides my face, and tell me truly what lies beneath. Am I beautiful or am I plain? Which?

(*The* VOICES *are heard*)

LIGHT VOICES (*off*) Beautiful—beautiful—beautiful . . .
DARK VOICES (*off*) Plain—plain—plain . . .
QUEEN. Well, Hans? What is your answer?

(HANS *looks round at the statues as though for advice*)

It's no use appealing to them for help. As you have heard, they cannot even agree among themselves. Well?

HANS (*moving up* C) I'm confused—I don't know—I can't think clearly. (*He moves* LC)

QUEEN. Well?

HANS. You have the air and manner of one who knows she is beautiful, and yet your voice is hard and cruel.

(*The* QUEEN *moves up* C *on to the dais and stands in front of her throne*)

QUEEN. I have given you longer than I gave any of the others. You must answer—now—or be turned to stone. (*She sits on the throne*)

HANS. I cannot believe you are ugly.

QUEEN. What, then, am I?

HANS. Beautiful. You are beautiful.

(*The* QUEEN *rises and moves to Hans*)

QUEEN. I knew what your answer would be the moment you entered my doors. My poor Hans! The incurable romantic who could not believe that a queen could be anything else but beautiful. (*She crosses down* L *of Hans and turns to face him, her back to the audience*) Look at me, Hans. Look at me and see why you have failed.

(HANS *faces the Queen*)

(*She removes her mask*) Do you see? Do you see, now?

HANS. Yes, I see. I was wrong; you should be beautiful, but you are not.

(*The* QUEEN *replaces her mask*)

QUEEN (*with a step towards Hans*) You almost make me feel

sorry for you, Hans. I could almost let you go—(*she moves nearer to him*) but you now know my secret, and you must not be allowed to reveal it. (*She moves close to him*) You do understand, don't you? (*She pauses*) Why don't you answer me, Hans? (*She touches his cheek*) How cold you are. As cold as stone—as cold as stone—as cold as stone. (*She turns from him, moves up* c *and sits on her throne*)

The Lights *fade slowly except for a spot on the motionless figure of* Hans. *Presently his voice, softly at first, then louder, comes out of the air, calling:* "*Alicia—Alicia . . .*" *The voice continues as—*

the Curtain *slowly falls*

ACT III

SCENE I

SCENE—*The Forest.*
The Scene is played in front of the downstage gauze TABS.

When the CURTAIN *rises,* SYLVESTER *is sitting on the fence down* L, *doing some tatting. The* PRINCESS *is dancing. When she finishes she looks off* L.

PRINCESS. Sylvester.
SYLVESTER. Yes, Princess?
PRINCESS. How long has Hans been in there, now?
SYLVESTER. About half an hour, I should think.
PRINCESS. I do hope he's all right. (*She moves towards Sylvester*) What are you doing?
SYLVESTER. Oh, just a bit of tatting to pass the time.
PRINCESS. What are you making?
SYLVESTER. It's a new lace collar for Hunk. I make all their things, you know. I have to. The Queen never gives me a penny for them. She's so mean you wouldn't believe.
PRINCESS (*moving close to Sylvester*) Sylvester—what sort of woman is she?
SYLVESTER. Who, the Queen?
PRINCESS. Yes; what does she look like, I mean?
SYLVESTER. I really don't know. I've never seen her without her mask, you know.
PRINCESS. Her mask?
SYLVESTER. Yes, didn't I tell you? She always wears it. It's gold, of all things. Now, an *ivory* and gold one might have been rather attractive.
PRINCESS. But why does she wear a mask?
SYLVESTER. Well, now, there are various opinions on that point. *I* think she just does it for effect—just to make herself look more mysterious. (*He tries the collar on the Princess*) I hope this is going to be big enough—you've no idea how those little pigs grow (*He rises and moves up* C) I do hope Hans isn't going to be much longer—young Hank is sure to be hoinking his head off for a drink of water or something; he always does it the minute you put him to bed. They only do it to draw attention to themselves, you know, it's not because . . .
PRINCESS. Sylvester.
SYLVESTER. Yes?

PRINCESS. Do you really think the Queen will help us?

SYLVESTER. She will if she gets the right answer to her question, I expect.

PRINCESS. What question?

(SYLVESTER *looks off* R)

SYLVESTER (*turning to the Princess*) Didn't I tell you?

PRINCESS. No, you didn't. (*She crosses to Sylvester*)

SYLVESTER. But I told Hans before he went in. You mustn't have been listening.

PRINCESS. I don't think you told him anything except to be careful.

SYLVESTER. Oh, Lord! He *will* be in a fix.

PRINCESS. But what question will he be asked? Tell me.

SYLVESTER. The one she always asks people—and the one they always get wrong.

PRINCESS. For Heaven's sake, Sylvester, what question?

SYLVESTER. What? Oh, whether she's plain or pretty under her mask.

PRINCESS. What a stupid question, anyway. (*She moves down* L) As if it matters.

SYLVESTER. Oh, it doesn't matter, except that it gives her an excuse—(*he moves towards the Princess*) for turning people into stone. She likes doing that.

PRINCESS. Turning people . . . ! Sylvester! Do you mean to stand there and tell me Hans is in danger of being turned into stone—(*she moves to* L *of Sylvester*) this very minute, and—and you never told me?

SYLVESTER. Well, I didn't want you to worry.

PRINCESS. Worry! (*She crosses above Sylvester and goes down* R) What do you think I've been doing all this time you've been so busy with that stupid tatting? Enjoying myself?

SYLVESTER. Oh, now, wait a minute, I . . .

(*The* PRINCESS, *with an air of determination, marches* C)

Where are you going?

PRINCESS. I'm going there, of course.

SYLVESTER. But the Queen never gives more than one audience a year. You can't go in.

PRINCESS. We shall see whether I can or not.

SYLVESTER. Princess, you can't—you mustn't.

PRINCESS. Her Highness the Princess will *demand* an audience of the Queen—this minute.

(*The* PRINCESS *marches off* L. SYLVESTER *follows to* L, *then returns to* C)

SYLVESTER. The Queen will *dessicate* me for this, I know she will.

(HANK *and* HUNK *skip on* R, *using their ribbons as skipping-ropes.*
They skip around Sylvester)

And what, may I ask, is the meaning of this? I thought I gave
you strict instructions to stay in bed, the pair of you.

(HANK *and* HUNK *stop skipping and start hoinking*)

It was what? . . . Your hot-water bottles? . . . What about your
hot-water bottles? . . . They what? . . . They burst? . . . Well,
if you will persist in filling them with boiling water, what can
you expect? . . . Who did? . . . *I* did? . . . Oh, perhaps I did . . .
All right, I'm sorry . . . I said I'm sorry . . . Now, come here.
(*He takes hold of the ribbons*) Right back to bed the pair of you.
(*He leads them* R)

(HANK *and* HUNK *hoink protestingly*)

Oh, yes, you do. I'm having no more of this kind of thing.
KING (*off* L; *calling*) You, there! You, sir! Stop a minute.

(SYLVESTER, HANK *and* HUNK *stop and turn*)

SYLVESTER. Now, who can this be? (*He moves* RC)

(*The* KING *enters* L *and crosses to Sylvester*)

KING. Ah! Thank goodness for a different face.
SYLVESTER. Different from what?
KING. Different from those other two.
SYLVESTER. What other two?
KING. They keep following me. I can't shake them off. A
strange woman in a cape and a round man with spectacles.
They're getting on my nerves. And what's more, I can't find my
way out of this confounded wood. Do you know what I think?
SYLVESTER. No, what?
KING. I think we're all going round in circles.
SYLVESTER. I'm not going round in circles.
KING. You're not?
SYLVESTER. No.
KING. You mean you're not lost?
SYLVESTER. Not a bit.
KING. How extraordinary! You'll be telling me you know who
you are, next.
SYLVESTER. I do know who I am.
KING. You don't know how lucky you are. I don't know, and
those other two—they don't, either. I was beginning to think
nobody knows anything.
SYLVESTER (*turning to go*) Yes. Well, this is a fascinating con-
versation, and I hate to tear myself away from it, but I'm afraid
I must.
KING. No, don't go. I might meet *them* again, and I simply

couldn't bear it, I . . . (*He notices Hank and Hunk*) What are those—these?

SYLVESTER. Swine.

KING. Swine? Oh, pigs, you mean.

SYLVESTER. Pigs, if you like. I am their swineherd.

KING. Really? What have they got bows on for?

SYLVESTER. Look, I can't go into that now, I must be leaving.

KING. No, but—they've got collars on, as well. And ribbon.

SYLVESTER. Yes.

KING. Well, it's odd, isn't it—I mean—well, pigs?

(HANK *and* HUNK *hoink*)

SYLVESTER (*moving to* R *of the* King) My dear sir, these particular pigs are not odd. Unusual, yes, but not odd.

(HANK *and* HUNK *hoink*)

And I must warn you that they understand every word you say, and they are more than usually sensitive. So be careful.

HANK ⎫
HUNK ⎭ (*together*) Hoink! Hoink!

KING. I didn't mean to offend them, I'm sure.

SYLVESTER. Think no more about it.

(*The* QUEEN'S *voice is heard*)

QUEEN (*off; calling*) Syl-vest-er!

SYLVESTER (*calling*) Com-ing! (*To the* King) Now, I really have very little time, so let's not beat about the bush. What exactly do you want of me?

(HANK *crosses to* L *of the* King, HUNK *to* R *of him*)

KING. I wonder if you could tell me the direct route out of this wood, and back to where people are sane and normal and rational—and where pigs don't wear lace collars.

SYLVESTER. We'll ignore the latter half of that and concentrate on the first bit. I hate to have to tell you, but you will never get out of this wood at all until someone shows you the way. (*He moves* R) Sorry, but there it is.

(HANK *and* HUNK *cross to Sylvester*)

KING. Never get out of it?

SYLVESTER. Never.

KING. We shall just go round and round in circles for ever and ever?

SYLVESTER. For ever.

KING (*moving down stage*) Now, look here, my time is valuable —I can't just remember why, but it is—and I simply can't afford to waste it rambling about woods. I insist that you guide me out of it by the shortest possible path.

(SYLVESTER, *as he speaks, circles the King, finishing* R *of him.*
HANK *and* HUNK *follow*)

SYLVESTER. My dear sir, who and what you are I neither know
nor care . . .

(HANK *and* HUNK *interrupt with insistent hoinking*)

(*To Hank and Hunk*) Be quiet, or you won't have any truffles for
supper.

(HANK *and* HUNK *subside*)

And my time is every bit as valuable as yours. (*He bows*) Good day.
(*He turns with excessive hauteur, to go*)

(HANK *and* HUNK *at once begin to clamour, pointing excitedly off* L)

Oh, for goodness' sake, what is it, now?
    HANK ⎫
    HUNK ⎬ (*together*) Hoink! Hoink!
SYLVESTER. More people? Where? I shall never get to the
Queen at this rate.

(MRS CRABTREE, *distraught and dishevelled, totters on* L. *The*
KING *moves behind* SYLVESTER *and pushes him forward*)

Now, who in the world is this?
MRS CRABTREE (*crossing to* C; *to the King*) Thank goodness I've
caught up with you. You must protect me. There's a horrid
little man following me, with the wildest look in his eye. He keeps
calling and whistling in the most alarming manner; send him
away, *please*.
KING (*crossing to* LC) Will you kindly leave me alone, madam?
MRS CRABTREE. What?
KING. Leave me alone and stop following me about.
MRS CRABTREE. But aren't you going to protect me from him?
KING (*turning on Mrs Crabtree*) Looking at you, I should say it's
he who needs protecting.
MRS CRABTREE. Oh!
KING. Can you deny that for the past I-don't-know-how-long
you have been pursuing me through the trees, brandishing pieces
of stick and hallooing in the most unlady-like fashion?
MRS CRABTREE. But you don't understand. I was lost.
KING (*turning away*) Then kindly lose yourself again. You—
you unnerve me.
MRS CRABTREE (*circling the King*) Well! And I thought you
looked a gentleman. I can see I was wrong.
SYLVESTER. Sir! Madam! Please control yourselves. I cannot
have such distressing scenes in front of my little swine.
KING. Oh, confound your little swine!

SYLVESTER. Well, really! We are certainly not going to remain here to be insulted. (*He moves* R) Hank. Hunk. We shall leave.

(SCRATCH *enters* L. *He is dishevelled and minus his glasses*)

SCRATCH (*crossing to* C; *feebly and myopically*) People! Living people! Talk to me—speak to me.

MRS CRABTREE (*moving behind Sylvester*) Go away, you horrid little man.

(HANK *and* HUNK *move to* R *of Scratch. The* KING *stands down* L)

SCRATCH. I thought I should never catch up with you. I've been going round and round—it's dreadful.

KING. Haven't we all?

SCRATCH. You must help me. I'm lost, my memory's lost, and worst of all, my spectacles are lost. I—I think I'm going to cry.

(HANK *and* HUNK *move* R)

KING. Don't you dare!

SCRATCH. I can't help it—everything seems to be getting on top of me. I—I can't bear it any longer. Will nobody take me out of this awful forest?

(HANK *and* HUNK *clamour around Sylvester*)

SYLVESTER. No, Hank . . . No, Hunk . . . But, I can't—I really can't—the Queen will be furious . . . But she will, I tell you . . . Oh, very well, if you insist.

(HANK *and* HUNK *hoink noisily*)

Now, please, please stop hoinking.

(HANK *and* HUNK *subside*)

(*He crosses to the King*) Hank and Hunk say they are sorry for you all—I can't imagine why—and they seem to think I ought to help you. Though how I can help when I know nothing about you is something which rather defeats me.

(HANK *and* HUNK *cross to Sylvester*)

HANK. Hoink, hoink!
SYLVESTER. *You* know?
HUNK. Hoink!
SYLVESTER. Then why on earth didn't you speak up before this? You know, you *can* be trying at times.
HANK. Hoink, hoink, hoink! Hoink!
HUNK (*moving to* L *of the King*) Hoink, hoink!

(HANK *moves to* R *of Sylvester*)

SYLVESTER. You don't tell me. He says you are King Rufus.

King. King? Am I? I felt there was something out of the common run about me, you know. A king! Well, well!
Hank (*moving to Scratch*) Hoink!
Sylvester. He says you are Scratch. The King's private secretary.
Scratch. He said all that with just one hoink?
Sylvester. Yes.
Scratch. Fancy!
Hunk (*crossing to Mrs Crabtree*) Hoink!
Sylvester. And you, madam, appear to be Scratch's aunt, and you do something I didn't quite catch.
Hunk. *Hoink hoink!*
Sylvester. Dowses. That's it. She dowses. (*To Hank and Hunk*) Now, what are they doing here and why?

(Hank *and* Hunk *each and together hoink for some time, with considerable gesticulations and pointings to the King, Scratch and Mrs Crabtree, and to various points off stage.* Mrs Crabtree *crosses to Scratch*)

(*He listens gravely until they have finished*) You're quite sure?
Hank. Hoink!
Sylvester (*moving down* c) What a busy little bee Daisy has been today.

(Hank *and* Hunk *move* lc)

King (*moving to* r *of Sylvester*) What did they tell you?
Sylvester. Everything, I imagine. They're very thorough, I find.
King. Oh, jolly good! Aren't you going to tell us?
Sylvester. Oh, of course. It's like this . . .

(*The* Queen's *voice is heard, with rather more edge to it this time*)

Queen (*off; calling*) Syl-vest-er.

(Scratch *drops to his knees at Mrs Crabtree's feet*)

Sylvester. There she is again. I'm sorry, but there isn't time, now. Look, what you'd better do is set off, and I'll catch you up later. I *must* see what the Queen wants.
Scratch. I just want to go home.
Sylvester. You shall. (*He points* r) Go straight through that way, and keep the sun on your right-hand side. You won't go far wrong, and I'll soon catch you up. You understand?

(Scratch *rises. The* King *crosses to* Scratch *and* Mrs Crabtree, *leads them* r, *then stops and turns*)

King. Yes, only—you won't forget, will you?
Sylvester. I won't forget. 'Bye now. (*To Hank and Hunk*) Wave to them, dears. 'Bye.

(HANK *and* HUNK *wave.*
The KING, SCRATCH *and* MRS CRABTREE *exit* R)

What a collection! Ah well, it takes all sorts to make a world, I suppose.

SYLVESTER, HANK *and* HUNK *exit* L, *then the* LIGHTS *come up behind the gauze* TABS *on to the next scene.*

SCENE 2

SCENE—*The Grotto.*
When the LIGHTS *come up, the downstage gauze* TABS *open.* HANS *is still standing* LC, *rigidly statuesque. The* QUEEN *has gone. The* PRINCESS *marches determinedly in up* R. *The* VOICES *start up.*

LIGHT VOICES (*off*) Alicia—Alicia—Alicia . . .
DARK VOICES (*off*) Turn back—turn back—turn back . . .
PRINCESS. I shall do no such thing. Be quiet, whoever you are.

(*The* VOICES *cease*)

(*She runs to Hans*) Hans! Why are you standing there like that? Hans, do you hear me? (*She snaps her fingers in front of his face, and then takes him by the shoulders and shakes him*) Wake up, Hans! Wake up! It's me, Alicia!

(HANS *relaxes from his rigid pose, shakes his head and blinks*)

HANS. What? Who? Princess—(*he kneels*) what has happened? I—I was turned to stone by the Queen—wasn't I?
PRINCESS (*kneeling beside Hans*) Of course you weren't turned to stone—you only thought you were.
HANS. But, the Queen—the Queen of the Forest—she . . .
PRINCESS. I don't believe in the Queen of the Forest. I think she's a sham. Anyone who goes about all day in a mask *must* be something peculiar.
HANS (*rising*) Alicia—(*he helps the Princess to rise*) I mean, Princess—I've never seen you like this. You're—you're capable, you're confident—you're quite different.
PRINCESS. It's only because I thought you were in real danger that I had the courage to do something about it.
HANS. Alicia, you mean you . . . ?
PRINCESS. Never mind what I mean for the moment. Come, we must leave here.

(*The* PRINCESS *and* HANS *move down* R.
The QUEEN *enters up* L *and crosses to* C. *The* VOICES *are heard*)

ALL VOICES (*off*) The Queen—the Queen—the Queen . . .

QUEEN (*stamping her foot*) Oh, be quiet!

(*The* VOICES *cease. The* PRINCESS *and* HANS *turn to face the* Queen)

(*She turns on the Princess*) How dare you? How dare you enter my palace unbidden? Whoever you are, you shall pay for this!

PRINCESS. I don't think so.

QUEEN (*with a step towards the Princess*) What did you say to me?

HANS. Alicia, *please* be careful.

PRINCESS. I said "I don't think so".

QUEEN (*moving nearer to the Princess*) Don't you dare address me in that fashion. I am a queen, I'll have you remember.

PRINCESS (*moving towards the Queen*) I am not unacquainted with queens. I may be one myself some day. And I have always been given to understand that the first duty of a queen is to keep her temper.

HANS (*moving to* R *of the Princess*) Alicia!

QUEEN. I will turn you both to stone for this.

PRINCESS. I don't believe you could turn anyone to stone. You didn't succeed with Hans.

QUEEN. Can't I? (*She moves up* C *and turns*) You'll soon see. Let me remind you that everyone who enters my palace is bound to give an answer to a rather difficult question, and if they can't . . .

PRINCESS (*crossing to* L *of the Queen*) I will give you the answer now, and the question as well. You are going to ask me whether I think you are plain or pretty, aren't you? (*She pauses*) Aren't you?

QUEEN (*taken aback*) How—how did you know?

PRINCESS. Never mind how I know.

(*The* QUEEN *moves down* R)

Well, you might as well take off your mask and your mystery with it, because you are neither. (*She moves* C) Neither ugly nor beautiful. You are ordinary—just very, very ordinary.

(*The* QUEEN *advances on the Princess, fists raised in anger*)

That is not good enough for you, is it—so you make a mystery where no mystery exists, but you can't get away from it, can you?

(HANS *moves between the Queen and the Princess*)

You are ordinary, ordinary, ordinary.

(*The* QUEEN *stares at the Princess for a moment, then tears off her mask. It is true; she is undistinguished in any way in looks. She goes to her throne up* C, *turns and stands in front of it.* HANS *and the* PRINCESS *turn to face the Queen*)

QUEEN. Well, what are you waiting for? Take your precious Hans and go. Do you hear me? Go away. (*She bursts into tears, sits on her throne and buries her head in her hands*)

PRINCESS. Oh, Hans!

HANS. I think we'd better leave, now. It's going to take her some time to get over this.

PRINCESS (*moving* LC) I—I don't know what came over me—I feel sure I've never spoken to anyone like that before.

HANS. It won't have done her any harm, and it might have done her a great deal of good. Come on.

(HANS *and the* PRINCESS *cross to* R. *The* QUEEN, *with an effort, recovers herself and rises*)

QUEEN. Wait!

(HANS *and the* PRINCESS *stop and turn*)

I owe you something. Not because you answered my question correctly and it is therefore your right, but because for the first time I have seen myself for what I am. (*She moves down* LC) I shall never again wear the mask, nor use my powers to turn anyone to stone. Oh, yes, I can do that: in a few more hours you would not have been able to wake Hans merely by shaking him; you were too quick for me, Alicia. You needn't tell me what help you need from me——

(*The* PRINCESS *crosses above the Queen to* L *of her*)

—Hans has already done that.

(HANS *moves to* R *of the Queen*)

All I am going to do is to tell you the one thing Daisy Crowfoot fears most in this life—but I must whisper it to you; even the walls of my own Grotto may be her spies.

HANS *and the* PRINCESS *move in close to the* QUEEN *who whispers to them. The* LIGHTS BLACK-OUT *as*—

the gauze TABS *close*

SCENE 3

SCENE—*The Forest.*

The first part of the Scene is played in front of the downstage gauze TABS.

When the LIGHTS *come up,* CASTOR *is* LC, *and* SENNA *is* RC. *They are sweeping the ground with large brooms.* SENNA *pauses and leans on his broom.*

SENNA. Do you know what I think is the worst part of losing your memory?
CASTOR. What?
SENNA. Not being able to remember things.
CASTOR (*stopping work*) Yes, that's the worst part of it.
SENNA (*sweeping*) For instance, I can't remember if I had any breakfast. So I don't know whether I ought to feel hungry.
CASTOR. That's very confusing. (*He crosses to Senna*) And I'll tell you something else. I don't think we've had any dinner, either.
SENNA. No. The witch might have given us a bit of that onion soup we made for her. She's a selfish old . . .
CASTOR. Sh! She might be listening. (*He crosses quickly to* LC)
SENNA (*following Castor*) I don't think so. She's probably out collecting.
CASTOR. Collecting what?
SENNA. Deadly nightshade, I should think.
CASTOR. I wonder who we really are. I've a feeling I wasn't a housemaid.
SENNA. I'll tell you what. Let's look in our pockets and see if there's anything with a name on it.
CASTOR. That's a good idea. (*He moves down* C)

(SENNA *moves to* R *of Castor*)

We'll start with you, because you thought of it.
SENNA. All right. Hold my broom a minute.

(CASTOR *takes Senna's broom*)

(*He turns out his pockets and hands the various articles to Castor*)
CASTOR (*as he takes the articles*) Spectacles—bottle marked "poison"—mouth-organ—kidney pills—corn plaster—and two-pence halfpenny. Is that all?
SENNA. It seems to be.
CASTOR. H'm! Well, you're either a short-sighted rat-catcher with lumbago who plays the mouth-organ in his spare time, or an unsuccessful street musician with bad feet. Here. (*He returns the articles to Senna*) Let's see what I've got.

(SENNA *pockets the articles and holds the brooms as* CASTOR *empties his pockets and hands the items to Senna*)

Saw, carving knife, hatchet——
SENNA. You must have been a pork butcher.
CASTOR. —needle and thread——
SENNA. With a bit of cobbling on the side.
CASTOR. —and this. (*He produces a horn*)

SENNA. What is it?

CASTOR. I don't know. (*He shakes the horn, looks through it and blows down it*) Unless it's an ear-trumpet. (*He puts it to his ear*)

SENNA (*into the horn; loudly*) You're a deaf shoemaker—with a tendency to homicide.

(CASTOR *reacts*)

CASTOR (*producing the snuff-box*) There's something else here—a snuff-box. This might tell us something. (*He opens the box*) There's writing on it. It says:

> "Yesterday's is what it was,
> Tomorrow's is what it will be,
> Today's is what it is,
> What is it?"

SENNA. It doesn't make sense.

CASTOR (*absent-mindedly taking a pinch of snuff*) "Yesterday's is what it was . . ." Ah—ah—ah . . . (*He sneezes*)

VOICE (*off*) Bless you! Here is the news. Flash.

(SENNA, *in alarm, drops Castor's articles.* CASTOR *drops the snuff-box and clings to Senna*)

The Court is in *such* a tizz this morning—I *beg* your pardon, is greatly concerned—about the fact that neither the King's nor the Princess's bed have been slept in. It is rumoured that they have both been out all night. The Court is less concerned at the absence of Castor and Senna, the King's physicians; some even go so far as to hope it may be permanent. Little do they know that their present employer, Daisy the Witch, is after their blood over a little matter of burnt onion soup . . .

SENNA. Castor, it means *us*—it's talking about us.

CASTOR. Shut the box, quick.

(SENNA *shuts the box by cautiously stamping on it*)

We must get away from here, Senna, far away. I've had enough of witches for the time being.

(CASTOR *and* SENNA *pick up the scattered articles from the ground*)

SENNA. So've I. What do you think she'll do to us when she catches us?

(*The* LIGHTS *come up behind the gauze* TABS *revealing the wood with the cottage, and* DAISY, *standing* C, *with arms folded, ominously tapping one foot. The gauze* TABS *open.* CASTOR *and* SENNA, *down* C, *bending to pick up the various articles, do not see* DAISY, *who creeps up behind them*)

CASTOR. *If* she catches us, you mean. Well, *if* she does, I shall tell her in no uncertain terms just exactly what I think of her.

Do you know what I shall say to her? I shall say this: "Daisy
Crowfoot," I shall say, "you are without exception——

(SENNA *sees Daisy and taps Castor*)

—the meanest, mouldiest——

(SENNA *moves away* L)

—most miserablest maniac it has ever been my misfortune——

(DAISY *moves* R *of Castor*)

—to—to . . ." (*He realizes Daisy is there, and tails off into incoherence*)
DAISY (*snatching the broom from Castor*) Oh, I am, am I?

(CASTOR *runs* L)

(*She chases Castor*) You'll find out just how mean I can be. (*She
takes a swipe at Castor and Senna with the broom*)

(CASTOR *and* SENNA *dodge up* R)

(*She chases them*) Off with you . . .

       (CASTOR *and* SENNA *run off up* R.
       DAISY *pursues them off.*
       HANS *and the* PRINCESS *enter up* L *and cross to* C)

HANS. The noise seemed to be coming from here. I'm sure it
was Daisy's voice. Look, the cottage. I'm sure it wasn't here the
last time, yet everything else is the same.
PRINCESS (*crossing to the cottage*) It *is* Daisy's cottage, I'm sure.
Hans, let's look inside it.
HANS. Well . . .
PRINCESS. Why not? We're not doing any harm.
HANS (*crossing to the cottage door*) I think I'd better go first.
You stay here a moment.
PRINCESS. I'd rather come with you. I don't want to risk
losing you again.
HANS. All right. (*He opens the door, peers in and calls*) Anyone
there? Is there anyone at home? (*To the Princess*) There doesn't
seem to be any answer. Come on.

    (HANS *and the* PRINCESS *go into the cottage, leaving the door open.*
    DAISY *enters down* R, *somewhat out of breath, moves to the cottage
and leans heavily on the broom she still carries*)

DAISY. Oh, thunders in the index! It isn't worth it, you know,
Daisy girl, it just isn't worth the palpitations.
PRINCESS (*in the cottage*) Look, Hans.
DAISY (*turning to the cottage door*) What's this? Visitors? Oh,
lovely, lovely, lovely! Daisy's not had company for ever so long.
So she must keep them here for a nice long stay. Lock 'em in,
Daisy. (*She pulls the door to and locks it*) Licker, locker, hinge and

knocker—(*she darts to the shutters and closes them*) bolt and bar, and there you are. Now, let's think what to do with them. Burn the house down and roast 'em alive? No. Starve 'em to death? No. (*She glances off* R) By the pricking of my thumbs, something piggy this way comes. Out of it, Daisy girl; oh, what a pest people are.

> (DAISY *capers off* L.
> SYLVESTER, HANK *and* HUNK *enter up* R *and cross to* C. *A loud knocking comes from the cottage.* HANK *and* HUNK *stand* RC)

HANS (*in the cottage; calling*) Let us out! Open the door and let us out! Help! We're locked in.

SYLVESTER. Gracious me, what a to-do! There's simply no peace in the forest these days. A cottage? Now, who could have put that there? I'm sure it wasn't there this morning. And I must say it doesn't improve the place a bit. Rather tatty . . .

HANK }
HUNK } (*together*) Hoink, hoink!

SYLVESTER. Daisy's cottage? You don't say! Someone seems to have locked her in, by the sound of it.

> (HANK *and* HUNK *hoink*)

Not Daisy inside? Who can it be, then?

> (HANK *and* HUNK *hoink*)

Open it and find out. That's logical, at any rate. (*He crosses to the cottage door, unlocks and opens it then returns* C)

> (HANS *and the* PRINCESS *come out from the cottage.* HANS *carries a phial*)

HANS (*crossing to* L *of Sylvester*) Oh, it's you.

> (*The* PRINCESS *moves to* R *of Hank and Hunk*)

What do you mean by locking us in there like that?

SYLVESTER. There's gratitude for you. I let him out and he gets ebullient. (*He moves to* L *of Hank and Hunk*) Never a word of thanks. I did not lock you in.

HANS. Who did, then?

SYLVESTER. Daisy. If you ask me, you are very lucky we turned up.

HANS. Oh, I see. I beg your pardon.

SYLVESTER. Not at all. What's that you have in your hand?

HANS. I don't know, really. (*He moves to* L *of Sylvester*) There's lots of them in there. Rows and rows of them, all neatly labelled with people's names. I was just about to open one when the door slammed on us and we were locked in.

> (HANK *and* HUNK *cross and stand down* R)

SYLVESTER (*taking the phial*) Let me see it. (*He holds the phial up to the light*) How extraordinary! It has sort of pictures in it—

changing pictures—there's a young girl walking in a beautiful
garden—it's—why—(*he turns to the Princess*) it's you, my dear.
PRINCESS (*crossing to* R *of Sylvester*) Me?
SYLVESTER. Yes, and it has your name on the label. I do
believe it's your memory in here.
PRINCESS. Sylvester, I have my memory back at last.

(SYLVESTER *hands the phial to the Princess*)

Oh, but—how do I make it mine again?
SYLVESTER. I don't know; break the bottle, perhaps?
HANS. Or drink it? Are there no instructions on the label?
PRINCESS. I can't see any.
HANS. We mustn't do the wrong thing, or the Princess's
memory may be lost for ever.
PRINCESS. Can't we ask Hank and Hunk?
HANK. *Hoink!*
SYLVESTER. Of course. Why didn't we think of it? Well, Hank?

(HANK *turns away*)

Hunk?

(HUNK *turns away*)

They're sulking. You see how difficult they can be? All because
we didn't ask them first. (*He crosses to Hank and Hunk*) It's very
bad manners for little pigs to sulk, didn't you know that?

(HANK *and* HUNK *sulk even more*)

Look, this is very important to the Princess. I know we should
have asked you first, and we're sorry. There. Now, will you help?

(HANK *and* HUNK *ignore him*)

Oh, I give up. (*He moves up* RC)
PRINCESS (*crossing to Hank and Hunk*) Hank—Hunk—you
wouldn't like to see me suffering from loss of memory for the rest
of my life, would you?

(HANK *and* HUNK *hoink sulkily*)

I've never done you any harm, have I?

(HANK *and* HUNK *hoink sulkily*)

Well, then?

(HANK *looks at Hunk*)

HANK (*to Hunk*) Hoink?

(SYLVESTER *moves a little down* RC)

HUNK (*to Hank*) Hoink, hoink!

PRINCESS. Oh, thank you both; I knew you would help. Now, what do I do?

(HANK *and* HUNK *show her, with elaborate mime and a good deal of noise*)

Uncork the phial and sniff? Is that all?

HANK ⎱
HUNK ⎰ *(together)* Hoink!

(*The* PRINCESS *uncorks the phial and sniffs*)

PRINCESS. I'm beginning to remember. I can! I can remember everything. Oh, Hank, Hunk, thank you; thank you so much. (*She kisses them*)

(HANK *and* HUNK *go into paroxysms of embarrassment*)

(*She turns to Hans*) Hans, I can remember it all again.

(HANS *swings the Princess to* C. SYLVESTER *crosses above the others to* LC)

All the lovely memories I thought were gone for ever. I can't begin to thank you enough.

(HANK *and* HUNK *dance up and down*)

HANS. It's wonderful to see you so happy. We must collect all the bottles and give them to their owners. There must be hundreds in there.

(MRS CRABTREE *enters* L *and crosses to* L *of Hans*)

Mrs Crabtree! Are you alone? Where's the King?

MRS CRABTREE. King? What King? I don't know what you're talking about.

SYLVESTER. But you were with him, don't you remember? And the secretary, too.

MRS CRABTREE. Oh, please. Please don't ask me any questions. I don't know the answer to anything.

SYLVESTER. But I told you to keep the sun on your right and you'd soon be out of the forest. You must remember that.

MRS CRABTREE (*moving to* R *of Sylvester*) Yes, I know, but they would *argue*. None of us could remember if you said right or left, and I got so tired of them brow-beating each other that I left them and came on alone. And I'm so tired all I want to do is to sit down and die.

PRINCESS (*crossing to* R *of Mrs Crabtree*) Hans, see if there's a bottle in there with her name on it.

HANS (*crossing to the cottage door*) Of course. Daisy must have taken her memory as well.

(HANS *and* HUNK *move to the cottage window*)

SYLVESTER. Oh, she has. *And* the King's. *And* Scratch's.
HANS. Good Lord: she's nothing if not wholesale.

(HANS *goes into the cottage and comes out in a few moments, carrying a phial*)

Here we are! "Mrs Crabtree. The Recollections of a Dowser."
(*He crosses and hands the phial to Mrs Crabtree*) Open it and sniff it.
(*He moves* c)
MRS CRABTREE. Sniff it? What for?

(*The* PRINCESS *crosses to* R *of Hans*)

HANS. Never mind why, just do it.

(MRS CRABTREE *opens the phial and sniffs. Her face lights up.*
SYLVESTER *moves up* LC. HANK *and* HUNK *open the shutters and look into the cottage*)

MRS CRABTREE. It—it all comes back to me—I remember it all—the Princess, the King . . . Oh! Oh, my goodness!
PRINCESS. What's the matter?
MRS CRABTREE. The King—will he ever forgive me?
HANS. Forgive you for what?
MRS CRABTREE. I—I chased him. I chased him through the forest for miles. I—I was horribly rude to him; I shall never live it down, never.
HANS. Of course you will. We shall all laugh at this tomorrow.
MRS CRABTREE (*moving to* L *of Hans*) Then you must have a very odd sense of humour, young man. (*She looks at Hans*) And now I come to think of it, what are you doing at liberty? (*She backs down* L) You should be under close guard in the palace for causing all this.
HANS (*crossing to Mrs Crabtree*) You've got it wrong, Mrs C. Daisy Crowfoot, a witch, is the cause of all this, not I.
MRS CRABTREE. A witch? (*She crosses to* c) I thought as much. Didn't I say so from the very first?
HANS. Well, anyway, whether you did or not, she still has to be reckoned with. As long as she's at liberty, she's a menace to us all. She's raving mad.
PRINCESS. She's got to be stopped.
MRS CRABTREE. Say no more. Crabtree is herself again. (*She moves down* c) Crabtree always . . .
PRINCESS ⎱ (*together*) Gets her witch! We know.
HANS ⎰
PRINCESS. What are you going to do?
MRS CRABTREE. When the divining rod fails, there is only one thing for it—the Crabtree Patent Witch-Trap, copyright reserved.
SYLVESTER (*moving above Mrs Crabtree*) A witch-trap?
MRS CRABTREE. Exactly.

HANS (*moving to* L *of Mrs Crabtree*) But how do we do it?

(*The* PRINCESS *moves to* R *of Mrs Crabtree.* HANK *and* HUNK *pay attention*)

MRS CRABTREE. It's very simple. First, we shall need a bowl of water from the cottage, and some salt.
HANS. I'll get that.

(HANS *crosses and goes into the cottage.* HANK *and* HUNK *move down* RC. SYLVESTER *moves to* L *of Mrs Crabtree*)

MRS CRABTREE. Next we need a piece of bright gold—a coin or something of that sort.
PRINCESS. I have a gold ring—will that do?
MRS CRABTREE. Excellently.

(*The* PRINCESS *hands her ring to Mrs Crabtree.*
       HANS *comes from the cottage with a bowl of water and a salt-cellar*)

HANS (*crossing to Mrs Crabtree*) Here's the water and the salt.
MRS CRABTREE (*taking the bowl*) That's it. (*She places the bowl on the ground* C) Now, we place the bowl on the ground, so. (*She takes the salt-cellar and sprinkles salt in and around the bowl*) We sprinkle the salt around it, so. (*She drops the ring into the bowl*) Then we pop the gold ring into the water. There we are, glittering nicely and looking most tempting.
SYLVESTER. What happens now?
MRS CRABTREE. Now, we disperse and wait.
PRINCESS. But how can this trap a witch?
MRS CRABTREE. Well, I don't know if you are aware of it, but all the power of a witch resides in her right thumb, but she must never put it into salt water. Now, the ring is the bait for the trap. No witch can resist the gleam of gold——

(HANK *and* HUNK *move up* C)

—and as soon as Daisy puts her hand in the water, her power is gone, and furthermore, she will be quite unable to pull her thumb out again. There she will be—trapped, as, sooner or later, is every witch who crosses the path of Hypatia Crabtree.
PRINCESS. What if Daisy happens to be left-handed?
MRS CRABTREE. Of course, if you are going to *make* difficulties . . .
HANK ⎱
HUNK ⎰ (*together; very agitated*) Hoink, hoink!
SYLVESTER (*moving up* C) What, sweeties?

(HANK *and* HUNK *hoink*)

(*He moves down* C) They say she's coming back.

MRS CRABTREE. Capital! (*She grabs Sylvester and Hans*) Now, we shall see what we shall see. Out of sight, all of you. Quickly, please. (*She goes down* R)

(HANS *moves to the upstage end of the cottage.* SYLVESTER *takes* HUNK *down* L. *The* PRINCESS *takes* HANK *behind the tree.* HANK *and* HUNK *hoink*)

SYLVESTER
MRS CRABTREE } (*together*) Ssh!

(*The* PRINCESS *crosses to Hans.* HUNK *runs to Hank.* SYLVESTER *starts to follow Hunk, but* MRS CRABTREE *pulls him down* R. *They all hide.*
DAISY *enters cautiously down* L, *sees the bowl, crosses to it and walks suspiciously round it*)

DAISY. That's odd, you know. That there bowl never got *there* by itself. Water in it, too. And something shining at the bottom. Gold! Thou glittering tempter! Lovely yellow shiny gold. I never could resist it, particularly other people's. (*She pushes up her right sleeve and stretches out her hand to the bowl*)

(*Six heads look out from the hiding-places, but rapidly disappear as* DAISY *pauses and looks around*)

(*She decides that no-one is about, and is just going to plunge her hand in the bowl, when she stops*) Wait! What's this on the ground? Salt! It is! Grains of salt or my name isn't Daisy. La Crabtree has been at it again. Oh, palpitations and goose pimples all over. She nearly had you that time, Daisy lass. But Daisy wasn't born yesterday, oh, dear no. I'll show that Crabtree. (*She picks up the bowl, drinks the water, takes the ring out of her mouth, wipes it and pops it on her finger*) So. Rings on her fingers and bells on her toes. She shall have magic wherever she goes. You know, it was *nice* of them to give me a ring.

(DAISY *goes into the cottage, leaving the door open. The others emerge, crestfallen, and none more so than* MRS CRABTREE. HANS *and the* PRINCESS *stand up* RC. HANK *and* HUNK *move* C. SYLVESTER *crosses to Hank and Hunk. They all stare at Mrs Crabtree*)

MRS CRABTREE (*crossing down* L) All right, say it. Don't just stand there glowering at me like that. I've failed. There is only one thing left for me to do. I shall return my badge to the League first thing tomorrow morning, and then—then join the Foreign Legion.
HANS. Sh!
MRS CRABTREE. What did you say?
HANS (*moving* C) I said "shush". Listen.

(*The* PRINCESS *moves to Sylvester*)

Daisy has trapped herself. All we have to do is lock her in. But quietly. Sh! Stay here. (*He tiptoes to the cottage, slams the door and locks it, then closes the shutters*) Licker, locker, hinge and knocker. Bolt and bar and there you are. Now, Mrs C. How's that for a trapped witch?

MRS CRABTREE (*crossing to* c) Really, young man, if you suppose for a moment that a witch can be caught as easily and straightforwardly as that, then you know very little about witches. She'll be out of there before you can say "knife".

HANS. Will she? Wait and see. (*He knocks on the cottage door and calls*) Daisy! Are you listening, Daisy Witch?

DAISY (*inside the cottage*) I'm listening, Hans Cleverclogs. And I'm telling you something, as well. If you're not out of this forest in two shakes, I'll turn you all into cockroaches. Be off!

HANS. Bravado won't get you anywhere now, Daisy. The game is up. The water was poisoned, didn't you know? Unless I give you the antidote you'll be dead inside a minute. I give you thirty seconds of life, Daisy Crowfoot—thirty seconds.

DAISY. Go away!

HANS. Is that your final answer?

DAISY. Yes, it is.

HANS. Fifteen seconds.

DAISY. You're wasting your time. (*Uncertainly*) There's nothing wrong with Daisy.

HANS. Ten seconds. Nine—eight—seven—six—five—four—three . . .

(*The shutters fly open and* DAISY's *face appears at the window.* MRS CRABTREE *goes down* L. SYLVESTER *and the* PRINCESS *go behind the tree.* HANK *and* HUNK *move above the cottage*)

DAISY. Stop! I don't feel well. Give me the antidote.

HANS. Give me the bottles first—quick—you haven't much time.

DAISY. Oh. (*She disappears from the window then reappears rapidly with two phials*) Here—take them. (*She hands the phials to Hans*)

HANS (*reading the labels*) "King Rufus." "Scratch the Secretary." What about the rest?

DAISY. You shall have them; give me the medicine, quickly—I feel quite dreadful.

HANS. Your promise?

DAISY. Yes, yes, I promise. Oh, I'm dying, I tell you, dying.

HANS. Your promise isn't good enough. Come outside.

DAISY. I—I can't; I'm too weak.

HANS. Outside, Daisy.

DAISY. Oh, you're a cruel, cruel young man. (*She goes from the window*)

(HANS *moves* c. MRS CRABTREE *moves* LC)

Hans (*to Mrs Crabtree; rapidly*) I don't trust her. Make her give a promise that's really binding on a witch. Can you do it?

Mrs Crabtree. Of course. Leave it to me.

> (Hans *unlocks the cottage door.*
> Daisy *totters from the cottage.*
> Hank *and* Hunk *exit up* R)

Daisy (*crossing to* C; *clutching her stomach*) Oh, I feel dreadful, quite dreadful. Please give me the antidote.

Mrs Crabtree. Now, please pull yourself together, my good woman. You're not dead yet. You must promise to practise no more magic in this kingdom.

Daisy (*kneeling; weakly*) I promise.

Mrs Crabtree. Nod to the east.

> (Daisy *nods*)

Wink to the west.

> (Daisy *winks*)

Bow to the north and curtsy to the south.

> (Daisy *rises and can just manage it*)

Daisy. And now—m-may I have the antidote?

Hans. Certainly. (*He moves to Daisy and whispers in her ear*)

Daisy. What? You mean I'm *not* poisoned? Oh! Oh! Oh! Oh! (*She stamps her foot, and beats the air with her fists in an agony of frustration*) You think you've beaten me, don't you? But, you haven't! You haven't! I'll—I'll . . .

Hans. What will you do?

Daisy. I'll turn the cottage into a tea-room.

> (Daisy *stamps into the cottage and slams the door. There is a puff of smoke and a clap of thunder, and the cottage disappears.*
> *The* Gobbin *enters down* R. *The others all turn to him*)

Gobbin (*grinning*) Hello.

Hans. Why, it's the Gobbin.

Gobbin. I've brought somebody to see you. (*He turns and beckons*)

> (*The* King *and* Scratch *enter down* R. *Each has one black eye and both are thoroughly dishevelled. The* King *crosses to* C)

Princess (*running to the King*) Father! Scratch! What on earth have you been doing?

King. Are you addressing me, madam? I'll have you know that I am a king. Two pigs told me.

Princess. Don't you know me?

King. I don't know *anything*.

Princess. I'm Alicia, dear. Hans, give him the phial, quickly.

(HANS *uncorks the phials and gives one to the King*)

HANS. Here you are, sir; sniff this and you'll be as right as rain. (*He hands a phial to Scratch*)
KING. Sniff it? I am a king—I shall inhale it.

(*The* KING *and* SCRATCH *sniff the phials. The light of intelligence returns to their faces*)

(*He turns to them one by one*) Mrs Crabtree—Hans, my dear boy—Alicia, my dear. (*He kisses the Princess then turns to Scratch and seizes him by the scruff of the neck*) Scratch!
SCRATCH. Sir?
KING (*pointing to his own black eye*) What about *this*?

(SCRATCH *begins to sniff as though about to cry*)

(*Hastily*) Oh, for heaven's sake, no, Scratch. I—I forgive you—I forgive you all, even Mrs Crabtree.

(*The* QUEEN's *voice is heard*)

QUEEN (*off; calling*) Syl-vest-er! Syl-vest-er!

(*All except the* KING *and* SYLVESTER *group* R *and* L)

KING (*moving* C) Who on earth *is* that?
SYLVESTER (*moving to* L *of the King*) It's me, sir. And that is the Queen, again. (*He bows*) I must go. (*He turns and moves up* L)

(*The* QUEEN *enters* L)

QUEEN (*as she enters*) Sylvester . . . (*She meets Sylvester* LC) Oh, there you are. (*She brings Sylvester* C) I'm so glad I have found you all together like this. Alicia, I want to thank you for helping me to know myself.

(*The* KING *coughs*)

SYLVESTER (*to the Queen*) Your Majesty, may I introduce his Majesty, King Rufus.
KING. How do you do?

(*All bow first to the King, then to the Queen*)

QUEEN. May I invite you—all of you—to my grotto——

(*The upstage gauze* TABS *open revealing the Grotto dais set with a buffet table with sandwiches, cakes, etc.* CASTOR *and* SENNA *are standing behind the table. The* PRINCESS *runs to Hans*)

—under completely new management—before you return to your palace.

(HANS *looks a little apprehensive*)

You need have no fear, Hans, you will not be turned into stone this time; nor will anyone else as long as I remain Queen of the Forest. (*She takes the King's hand and leads him up* C) Come.

(CASTOR *and* SENNA *move below the table with plates of sandwiches.* DAISY *enters* R *and moves up* C. *The others all congregate up* C, *except the* GOBBIN, *who turns to go.* HANS *turns and sees him*)

HANS (*crossing to the Gobbin*)   Hey, Gobbin!

(*The* GOBBIN *stops and turns*)

Aren't you coming, too?

GOBBIN (*writhing bashfully*)   I don't like.

HANS. Oh, come on. We want you.

GOBBIN. Is it a knife and fork do?

HANS. Oh, I expect so.

GOBBIN. Ask me again, then.

HANS. Gobbin, will you please join us for supper—a knife and fork do?

GOBBIN. Ee, you make me feel proper awful.

The GOBBIN *lumbers up* C. HANS *follows him as*—

the CURTAIN *falls*

FURNITURE AND PROPERTY LIST

PROLOGUE

On stage: Tree

Off stage: Knapsack. *In it:* bread, cheese, liver sausage (HANS)

ACT I

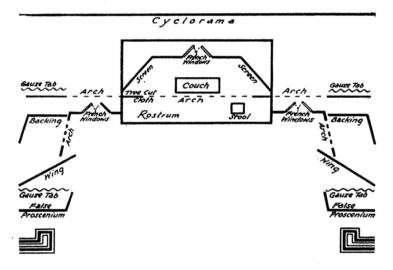

On stage: Couch on castors. *On it:* cover, decorative cord
            Stool

Off stage: Notebook, pencil (SCRATCH)
            Forked hazel stick (MRS CRABTREE)

Personal: DAISY: snuff-box
            MRS CRABTREE: badge
            SENNA: handkerchief
            SCRATCH: spectacles

ACT II

SCENE I

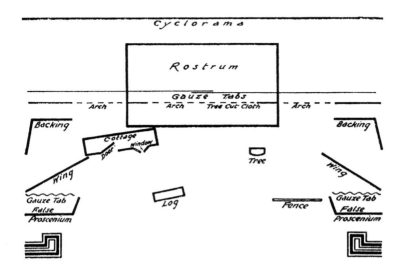

On stage: Log (c)
Tree. *Behind it:* butterfly net
Fence

Off stage: Red herring (DAISY)
Hazel twig (MRS CRABTREE)
Bundle of sticks (DAISY)
Stool. *On it:* cup of tea, glass phial (DAISY)
Butterfly net (DAISY)
Bowl of onions, 2 knives (DAISY)

SCENE 2

In front of gauze TABS

SCENE 3

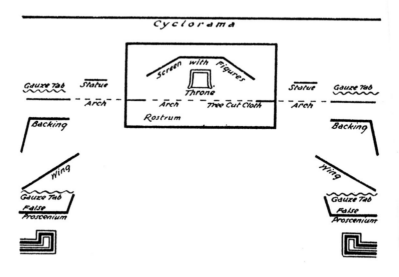

On stage: Throne
Statues

ACT III

SCENE 1

In front of gauze TABS

Off stage: Tatting (SYLVESTER)

SCENE 2

The Grotto

SCENE 3

In front of gauze TABS

Off stage: 2 brooms (SENNA and CASTOR)
2 Phials (HANS)

Bowl of water, salt-cellar (HANS)

2 phials (DAISY)

On Grotto dais: Buffet table with sandwiches, cakes, etc.

Personal: SENNA: spectacles, poison bottle, mouth-organ, box of pills, packet of corn plaster, coins

CASTOR: saw, carving knife, hatchet, needle and thread, horn, snuff-box

PRINCESS: gold ring

LIGHTING PLOT

Property fittings required: none

PROLOGUE. Exterior. A Royal Park

> THE APPARENT SOURCE OF LIGHT is daylight
> THE MAIN ACTING AREAS are RC, C and LC

To open: Effect of daylight
BLACK-OUT behind gauze backings

Cue 1   GOBBIN: "Gobbin, gobbin, gobbin."   **(Page 4)**
Bring up spot behind downstage gauze to illuminate Princess on couch

Cue 2   GOBBIN: "Gobbin this road . . ."   **(Page 5)**
Fade spot behind gauze

Cue 3   GOBBIN: ". . . in two ticks."   **(Page 5)**
Dim all lights to BLACK-OUT

ACT I.   Interior. A Palace room

> THE APPARENT SOURCES OF LIGHT are windows up RC, up C and up LC
> THE MAIN ACTING AREAS are up C, RC, C and LC

Pre-set to open: Effect of daylight

Cue 4   When gauze TABS open   **(Page 6)**
Bring up lights as pre-set

ACT II, SCENE 1.   Exterior. The Forest

> THE APPARENT SOURCE OF LIGHT is daylight
> THE MAIN ACTING AREAS are RC, up C, at a tree up LC and at a log seat C

To open: Effect of daylight
BLACK-OUT behind upstage gauze TABS

Cue 5   At end of Scene when gauze downstage TABS close **(Page 42)**
BLACK-OUT *behind* TABS

ACT II, SCENE 2.   In front of gauze TABS

To open: Effect of gloomy daylight

Cue 6   At end of Scene   **(Page 45)**
Dim all lights to BLACK-OUT

ACT II, SCENE 3.   Interior. The Grotto

> THE APPARENT SOURCE OF LIGHT is daylight
> THE MAIN ACTING AREAS are C, and at a throne up C

Pre-set to open: Effect of sombre interior lighting

Cue 7   After SYLVESTER and the PRINCESS exit   (Page 45)
     Bring up lights as pre-set

Cue 8   The QUEEN sits on the throne   (Page 48)
     Dim all lights to BLACK-OUT except for a spot on Hans

ACT III, SCENE 1.   In front of the gauze TABS

To open: Effect of gloomy daylight
         BLACK-OUT behind downstage gauze TABS
Cue 9   SYLVESTER, HANK and HUNK exit   (Page 56)
     Bring up lights behind downstage gauze TABS

ACT III, SCENE 2.   The Grotto

To open: Lighting as ACT II, SCENE 3
Cue 10   The QUEEN whispers   (Page 58)
     Dim all lights to BLACK-OUT

ACT III, SCENE 3.   In front of the gauze TABS

To open: Effect of gloomy daylight
         Black-Out behind downstage gauze
Cue 11   SENNA: ". . she catches us?"   (Page 60)
     Bring up lights behind gauze TABS

EFFECTS PLOT

PROLOGUE

ACT I

ACT II

SCENE 1

SCENE 2

SCENE 3

ACT III

SCENE 1

No cues   SCENE 2

                                         SCENE 3

Cue 6   DAISY exits into cottage   (Page 69)
               Puff of smoke and clap of thunder

Printed and bound in Great Britain by
Antony Rowe Ltd, Chippenham, Wiltshire